GEOLOGY EXPLAINED IN
NORTH WALES

GEOLOGY EXPLAINED IN NORTH WALES

by
JOHN CHALLINOR
and
DENIS E. B. BATES

With a chapter by
Professor Emeritus E. G. Bowen

DAVID & CHARLES : NEWTON ABBOT

ISBN 0 7153 5942 8

Set in 10/12 Pilgrim
and printed in Great Britain
by W. J. Holman Limited Dawlish
for David & Charles (Holdings) Limited
South Devon House Newton Abbot Devon

Contents

Preface

North Wales is one of the great 'classic' regions of geology; it has long been famous for its beautiful examples of some of the most striking geological phenomena and its treasures seem inexhaustible. Here indeed is 'Geology Observed' and here we may hope to have 'Geology Explained'.

The purpose of this book is twofold. In the first place it aims at being an introduction to geology by taking examples from one particular region. Secondly it aims at providing a guide towards the understanding of the geology of that region.

As in the other books in this series a leading feature is that of the anotated sketches, maps, sections, and views. The Bibliography section, a list of the works referred to, is fairly comprehensive. In turning up these references, as occasion and opportunity offer, the reader may be inspired to pursue geology into some of its inner recesses where lie many of its chief pleasures.

The more technical terms are defined in the Glossary, though in most cases there are also incidental explanations as the terms are used.

The regional accounts have been taken in an order which seems the best for unfolding our explanations of the geology of North Wales. Those of the north Cardiganshire and Anglesey regions are rather fuller than those of the others, primarily because they are well contrasted, geologically and geographically, and provide, each in its own way, exceptionally interesting geological phenomena and problems. Incidentally, these are the regions that have been specially investigated by the authors. The Anglesey section is written by D.E.B.B., all the rest of the main text by J.C. All the sketches are drawn by D.E.B.B.

A special additional chapter, 'Geology and Man in North Wales', has been very kindly contributed by Professor Emeritus

E. G. Bowen. In a few places this repeats facts that have been given in the various regional sections; but such minor bits of overlapping are all to the good as several of the more interesting 'human' points are thereby emphasised. This valuable essay is kept intact as written, quite independently, by its distinguished author.

The authors of this book are obviously greatly indebted to all the authors and publishers referred to and they hope that all concerned will accept this general acknowledgement. Special permission has been granted to quote the extensive excerpt on volcanic activity from Professor Rast's paper in *Nature in Wales*.

J.C. and D.E.B.B.

CHAPTER 1

Principles of Geology

Rocks

When we see or think of a piece of country, particularly a piece of hilly country like North Wales, it is clear that there are three elements present: the works of man (buildings, roads); the vegetation (woods, pastures) including the soil on which it grows; and the form and substance of the land. The substance of the land will be largely covered up, but everyone knows that it must be there.

The first thing to be noticed is that this substance is usually of two very different kinds: (1) the loose sands, silts, clays, and muds, and (2) the solid masses of stone. Further, it is realised that where there are materials of the first kind they overlie materials of the second which are everywhere present if we dig deep enough. The superficial deposits overlie the solid masses.

It is unfortunate that there is no satisfactory term for all these materials; the scientist simply calls them all 'rocks'. A rock has been defined as 'an aggregate of mineral particles', and this is probably as good a definition as any.

Nowhere could we find a better country than North Wales for displaying a variety of these two categories of rocks. Of the first category there are the alluvial deposits of the valleys, laid down by the rivers. There are also more widespread deposits— clays with boulders and stones, and sands—which are not at first sight obviously to be accounted for. (We shall see later that these are of glacial origin). More striking in the view and more challenging in their call for investigation are the bare solid rock masses exposed in the mountain precipices and the sea cliffs. Man, also, repays some of the debt he owes for covering things over by making excavations.

The study of all the different kinds of rock in themselves—(1)

what mineral substances they are made of, the sizes and shapes of the component particles, and how they are arranged and fitted together; and (2) what they may teach as to how they were formed—is the science of *petrology*, the science of rocks.

Sedimentary rocks—fossils

We shall mostly be concerned with the hard solid rock masses which underlie everything else though they may be only locally exposed.

It is obvious, from the most casual inspection of these rocks, revealed here and there throughout our region, that they are of different kinds—they differ in their *lithological* character. Petrology, and indeed common sense, tells us that many, if not most, of these are hardened sands and muds, *sandstones* and *mudstones*. In North Wales the roads are so often cut through solid rock that excellent sections of these can be conveniently seen. Wider research would show that the several varieties occurred as distinct masses, and that these were broadly extended, one lying over another, and that there is a succession, an order of superposition, of such sheets. The sheets themselves are stratified, being made up of layers—strata or beds. We conclude therefore that we here have rocks, *sedimentary* rocks, which represent successive depositions of sediments during successive periods of time.

The above conclusion is confirmed when we find remains of sea-shells in these rocks. The remains of these shells and of other forms of life preserved in the rocks are fossils. The study of fossils is called *palaeontology*, the science of the life of past geological ages.

Igneous rocks

In North Wales we should soon find rocks, interbedded among the ordinary sediments, that are, both to the eye and to petrological examination, evidently *volcanic* rocks—the extrusive products of old volcanoes. Other North Wales rocks, composed of a mosaic of conspicuous crystals, are not matched by any process we can observe today but the sciences of chemistry and physics tell us that they must also have been formed by cooling, in this case slow cooling, from a molten state. This consideration, together with the way in which they are associated with the sedimentary rocks, leads to the conclusion that they have become solidified within the earth's crust, molten *magma* having forced its way among these pre-existing rocks but not reaching the surface. These are the *intrusive* rocks. Both the volcanic and the intrusive rocks constitute the great class of the *igneous* rocks. Our region provides as good examples of all kinds of igneous rocks as any part of the world of comparable size.

Structure

In saying that the broad masses or sheets of sedimentary rock may be found to be lying one on another we have anticipated that the recognition of this is due, in any extended sense, to the fact that these masses are generally tilted to a greater or less degree; they are said to *dip* in a certain direction and to a certain amount. The direction in which the beds keep the same level, the direction at right angles to the dip, is the direction of *strike*. In some places *folds* of the strata are to be seen, and sharp breaks—*faults*. Thus the present geological structure of a region, such as we have in North Wales, is in the main an original arrangement of rock-sheets which have been later deformed as a result of stresses in the earth's crust.

The one fundamental simple conception to grasp is that we are dealing with three-dimensional structures. Not only are we to picture, so far as the observed facts allow, the rocks as they are, below the surface, but we are also to imagine them as extending far above this surface into the region from which they have been worn away.

Slaty cleavage—metamorphism

Another important effect of these stresses is the production of *slaty cleavage* within the finer-grained rocks. This is a reconstitution and re-orientation of the minute mineral particles so that they become flakes disposed at right angles to the pressure. The rock tends to break in the direction of these new planes instead of along the planes of the original bedding. The degree to which this cleavage is developed depends on the conditions of pressure and of rock composition and structure. North Wales is famous for its wealth of fine slates which have a perfect cleavage.

Alteration, recrystallisation, of the rock-substance by extreme pressure or the heat of an igneous intrusion, or by both pressure and heat combined, may go so far as to produce a rock entirely different from the original, whatever that might have been. These rocks are the *metamorphic* rocks. Here again North Wales, particularly Anglesey, shows many different varieties.

Geomorphology

The science of *geomorphology* studies the form of the land, its relation to the underlying structure and the working of those processes which are all the time modifying it. These processes comprise chiefly the action of weathering, rivers, ice, and the sea. Gradual movement (tilting, warping) of the upper part of the earth's crust would affect the standing of the general surface of the land. The dramatic landscape of North Wales clearly deserves to be appreciated to the full by being understood—by being explained.

Succession and correlation—the general table of strata—geological time

As a result of the piecing together of local successions we can eventually build up a whole column of strata embracing the lowest (oldest) to the uppermost (newest) anywhere found. However, owing to outcrops being disconnected and the kinds of rock, laid down as sediments at any one time, varying from place to place, this would be impossible were it not for the fortunate fact that contemporaneous rocks tend to be characterised by the same kinds of fossils. This results from the evolution of different forms of life throughout geological time. Suffice it to say here that on the fossil evidence rocks can be *correlated* from one region to another.

The whole *stratigraphical succession*, constituting a general table of strata, although really a continuous one, must be divided into named parts, if only for convenience. The main divisions are the stratigraphical systems which, to adopt the simplest classification, are as shown in the table on p13.

The Cambrian rocks are the lowest in which fossils of recognisable kinds have been found. All such tables, whatever the span embraced, are written with the lower divisions below the upper. Although this is primarily an arrangement of material bodies in space, it is also an arrangement of successive periods

Group (era)	System (period)	Millions of years
Cainozoic		70
Mesozoic	Cretaceous	135
	Jurassic	180
	Triassic	225
Upper Palaeozoic	Permian	275
	Carboniferous	350
	Devonian	400
Lower Palaeozoic	Silurian	435
	Ordovician	500
	Cambrian	600
	Pre-Cambrian	4,500

of time. Up to about fifty years ago, we could only guess the absolute lengths of time involved, but since then, and with ever increasing confidence and accuracy, the measurement of time in absolute terms of years has become possible by radiometric methods applied to the mineral constituents of rocks. In the above table the figures, based on the latest estimates, give the approximate age of the beginning of each period, in millions of years. The figure for the Pre-Cambrian is also the rough estimate of the age of the earth itself.

World-wide classification of the stratigraphical succession— the systems with their divisions and subdivisions—is based on the succession of widespread fossil faunas (and floras). Should radiometric methods ever become abundantly applicable and sufficiently accurate, direct time-correlation of rocks would then be possible.

The superficial deposits are the product of the last million years or so, a comparatively short and not specially significant period of time in the physical history of the earth. But to the observer of today the more recent happenings and products are the more completely and obviously evident and visible, particularly the deposits laid down on land. These, for the most part, are only temporary; they are being removed, particularly by rain-wash and rivers. This period has happened to be, however, one when glacial conditions were more widespread than they are today, so that we speak of it as an 'Ice Age'. In human history it is unique as being the period which saw the emergence of man.

Palaeogeographies and revolutionary changes
By examining the character and distribution of the rocks which

were formed at the successive periods of time we are able to infer the changing conditions during the geological history of a region which we now define by present geographical boundaries. The very fact that rocks originally laid down as deposits in the sea now form areas perhaps high in the heart of the land shows that there have been profound changes. We are led to reconstruct the geography, the *palaeogeography*, of successive periods of past time.

Deformation and metamorphism give evidence of profound changes in the earth's crust and the upheavals of its surface.

Geological processes—Uniformitarianism
All the time, in our observations and explanations, we have to study those geological processes that we can see in action today, particularly those which are wearing away the land and depositing material in the neighbouring sea. On the other hand, as we noted when mentioning the intrusive igneous rocks and when we were referring to the tilting, folding, and faulting of the rocks, there must be processes whose operations we cannot see or feel today (or get only hints of, as in earthquakes) either because they are out of sight or too slow. There is no reason to suppose that what is happening now has not always been happening and what has happened in the past is not happening today. This is the fundamental principle of *Uniformitarianism*, first definitively formulated by James Hutton towards the end of the eighteenth century.

Geology defined
We have now presented the outlines of this great comprehensive science of *Geology*, one which includes a number of component sciences. Geology involves three logical stages of investigation: observation of composition and structure, discussion of process, reconstruction of history.

The Geological Map
The most important representation of the geology of a region, large or small, is given by the *geological map*. The investigation of a region is begun by the making of such a map. Thus our accounts will be founded on and illustrated by geological maps.

The geological map shows primarily the areas of *outcrop* of the several rock-units. For the stratigraphical formations, observed dips will be recorded, particularly on the more detailed large-scale maps. These dips enable the order of superposition of the individual strata, and the rock-units they make up, to be determined. If the relative ages of two or more of the formations are known (from their fossils), then, if the outcrops follow in an orderly manner over the area, we know in which direction the rock-groups must underlie one another, apart from dips having been recorded. If, over fairly even ground, the outcrops are repeated in reverse order, this shows that the whole series must be folded. If newer rocks lie along the central line, there is a downfold, a *syncline*; if older rocks, an upfold, an *anticline*. If the outcrops are interrupted along a line, faulting is indicated. It may be that the completed map shows a boundary line of one formation cutting across the boundaries of a set of regularly arranged formation-outcrops. This line itself may be the first of another set of boundary lines running more or less parallel on the other side. This line is the most important feature of the map, being the outcrop of an *unconformity*. In such a case we have an upper series of formations which are unconformable to a lower. The upper series is discordant to the lower and overlies a truncated structure of that lower series. This discordant relationship results (as we quite certainly may infer) from the working of the geological cycle, a long-term repetition of the following conditions: (1) *deposition* of a pile of sediments in a sinking part of the sea; (2) *deformation* of these sediments by lateral compression and, presumably at the same time, *orogeny*, that is, uplift to form a mountainous land region; (3) lowering of this land region by *erosion and denudation*; (4) *submergence* beneath the sea with the accumulation of a new series of sediments on the eroded, truncated, edges of the old.

When we know the age of the lowest member of the upper series, the upper limit to the possible age of the deformation and orogeny is known. The lower limit to the possible age is given by the age of the highest rocks seen to be affected. The map will show the outcrops of any igneous intrusions and metamorphic rock-masses.

So far we have been considering only the rocks of the solid structure underlying the superficial deposits. These deposits hide the rocks underneath and it may seem a contradiction to speak of an 'outcrop' that does not appear at the surface. But in our 'solid' map we imagine the superficial deposits to be cleared away. Thus the boundaries on the solid map of the whole area must be conjectural (more, or less, certainly inferred) over those parts covered with superficial deposits. These various deposits must be mapped for their own sake and shown either on a separate map (usually called a 'drift' map) or by lines superimposed on the solid map.

The written account of the region will contain petrological, palaeontological, and structural details, with discussions of the processes involved and the geological history of the region.

CHAPTER 2

Summary of the Geology of North Wales

Succession

The stratigraphical systems present in North Wales are those ranging from the Pre-Cambrian to the Permo-Triassic inclusive. Their distribution is shown on our general map.

These systems, with their primary subdivisions, are tabulated below.

Permo-Triassic	New Red Sandstone
Carboniferous	Coal Measures Millstone Grit Carboniferous Limestone
Devonian	Old Red Sandstone
Silurian	Ludlow series Wenlock series Llandovery series
Ordovician	Upper Bala (Ashgill) series Lower Bala (Caradoc) series Llandeilo series Llanvirn series Arenig series
Cambrian	Upper (Tremadoc series) Upper (Lingula Flags) Middle Lower (including Arvonian)
Pre-Cambrian	Monian

Nomenclature

The whole of stratigraphical nomenclature is a mixture of different kinds of names and has grown by historical usage. The names of the systems as given in our table are used throughout the world, with linguistic modifications.

The rocks of the Cambrian system were first explored in our region by Adam Sedgwick, and those of the Silurian in the

B

Welsh Borderland and southern Wales by Roderick Murchison; both explorations were carried out in the 1830s. There was uncertainty and controversy as to where the statigraphical boundary between the Cambrian and the Silurian systems should be drawn. This was settled when Charles Lapworth proposed and defined the Ordovician system between the two in 1879. This was adopted not merely as a compromise but primarily because it was realised that these rocks constituted a succession which should on purely geological grounds be named as a separate system. The Silurian system was named from the ancient British tribe of the Silures who inhabited the south-eastern parts of Wales, and the Ordovician from the Ordovices who inhabited parts of northern Wales. Thus the three great systems of the Lower Palaeozoic were first investigated in Wales and the Borderland, from which they take their names.

Within the systems the succession in any region is classified on its merits, that is, according to the distinctively individual formations that are there recognisable. These are usually given local names, but when they are names given in a region where the system was first investigated they tend to have a wider application.

Many place-names in Wales have recently reverted to the original Welsh spelling. Fortunately, most of the names in our tables are unaffected, but, for instance, Arenig should be Arennig, Arvon should be Arfon, Dolgelley (or Dolgelly) should be Dolgellau, and Plynlimon should be Pumlumon. But the anglicised spellings are so firmly embedded in geological literature that it would be confusing if they were changed in our present account.

The Devonian system was first investigated in Devon, also by Sedgwick and Murchison, in this case working together. In Britain the rocks of this system belong to two distinct facies, the normal marine facies in Cornwall and South Devon and a non-marine or 'continental' facies, the Old Red Sandstone, elsewhere.

The Carboniferous system is so named from the occurrence in its upper part of nearly all the true coal seams of the world.

Breaks in the succession
The chief breaks in the succession are the following.

Between the Monian and other formations, Ordovician and later; the contact being in most cases clearly one of simple unconformity. While the Monian is therefore proved to be pre-Ordovician in age, the character of the rocks points to a Pre-Cambrian assignment.

There is a widespread unconformity at the base of the Ordovician although there is in some areas (Tremadoc, Dolgelley) what appears to be a continuous succession.

There are local unconformities in the Ordovician succession, but interpretations vary as to how great these are. There is generally a conformable passage up from the Ordovician into the Silurian.

The Old Red Sandstone of Anglesey rests unconformably on the Ordovician.

The Lower Carboniferous series rests everywhere unconformably on earlier formations.

There is unconformity at the base of the Permo-Triassic.

Structure
The whole of the Lower Palaeozoic formations have together been profoundly deformed structurally. They have been thrown into folds, broken by faults, and, when the lithology has allowed, been forced to take on slaty cleavage. The main structural lines are shown on our maps.

The Carboniferous Limestone series, resting everywhere on the mainland of North Wales unconformably on the strongly deformed Lower Palaeozoic rocks, is itself only gently tilted.

History
From the foregoing statements about the general structures of the Lower Palaeozoic rocks and the Carboniferous rocks it is clear that the deformation of the former occurred during some part of the Devonian period. It seems probable that the main deformation, at least, occurred at a time just after the end of the Silurian period, referred to as 'end-of-Silurian' or 'end-Silurian'.

In our outline of the main geological principles we have mentioned deformation and orogeny as, together, constituting one of the main phases of the geological cycle. In North Wales we have an excellent example of this; and we have also an excellent example of the preceding phase, the building up in a subsiding sea of a thick pile of sediments (here with igneous action during the middle period), destined to undergo this deformation and orogeny by being squeezed, after a prolonged period of sedimentation, as in the jaws of a vice by the pressure of movement in the upper part of the earth's crust. Such a subsiding region of the sea-floor—it is usually trough-shaped—is a geosyncline.

In the Welsh Borderland and in south-east Wales comparatively undisturbed upper Silurian strata pass up conformably into the Old Red Sandstone. Though there was a change in the geographical conditions under which the rocks were deposited there was no uplift and erosion of the Silurian before the deposition of the Old Red Sandstone.

The geosyncline, in which the Lower Palaeozoic rocks of what is now North and Central Wales were laid down, was aligned in a north-east to south-west direction with land-areas (or perhaps shallow 'shelf' seas) on its north-west and south-east sides where are now, respectively, the Irish Sea and the English Midlands.

> The long period (spanning about 200 million years) of slow subsidence and deposition marked by the Lower Palaeozoic geosyncline was followed by one of instability and intense earth-movement. The unconformities and contemporaneous oscillations of Lower Palaeozoic times were forerunners on a gentler scale of the grand folding and fracturing that occurred at the end of the Silurian period. (George)

The essential effect of this profound disturbance that occurred at the end of the Silurian period was the deformation of the rocks. This we can now actually see because of the dissection of the structures by erosion. What we can only conjecture is the accompanying orogeny, the production of a mountainous land.

By the end of Devonian times the mountain land had been much lowered by erosion and by about the middle of Lower Carboniferous times the sea spread from the north and east over the north-eastern part of what is now North Wales, laying down calcareous deposits, in clear water, on a slowly subsiding floor. This sea later became silted and shallowed to form a coastal swamp in which sands, muds, and deposits of vegetable debris accumulated in Upper Carboniferous times. Then, over much the same general area, came the desert New Red Sandstone deposits of Permo-Triassic age.

During the Carboniferous and Permo-Triassic periods most of what is now North Wales—that is, all except (very roughly) the counties of Denbigh and Flint—had remained dry land and from then on the geological history of the whole of North Wales is entirely unrecorded in the rock-archives. It is unlikely that the Jurassic Sea came into the region, except possibly into Anglesey and the extreme north and east, and it was certainly dry land, as was most of Britain, during the Lower Cretaceous period. There is a faint possibility that the Upper Cretaceous Sea, spreading far and wide over the British area, laid down some deposits, now entirely lost, over North Wales. At some time during the Tertiary era this 'North Wales' was uplifted to form a high land from which the present relief has evolved. The last episode was the Ice Age.

An 'ice age' or 'glacial period' is a time in earth history when glacial conditions were so much more extensive than they are today, or at least so differently placed, that they covered regions and extended down to levels now enjoying a temperate climate. There have been several, very infrequent, glacial periods throughout the geological history of the earth, but 'the Glacial Period', 'the Ice Age', 'the Great Ice Age', refer to that very recent one that may be said to have now vanished from Britain and northern Europe generally, but only so lately as some 10,000 years ago. It began at a time rather vaguely estimated as being of the order of 1,000,000 years ago and, again vaguely, as coinciding with the Pleistocene period, the latest part of the Cainozoic era.

The Ice Age as a whole comprised four or five minor ice ages, with more genial interglacial periods. Such oscillations however are hardly recognisable in North Wales.

Sources
These large general matters are what emerge after a century and a half of detailed research. There are several authoritative discussions and summaries, of which by far the most generally important is the official Regional Geology handbook (George, 1961). Others are the two addresses to the Geological Society by O. T. Jones (1938, 1955) and the two reviews by Bassett (1963, 1969). Structure is considered in detail by Shackleton (1953), and Thomas (1970) has illustrated the 'imprint of structural grain on

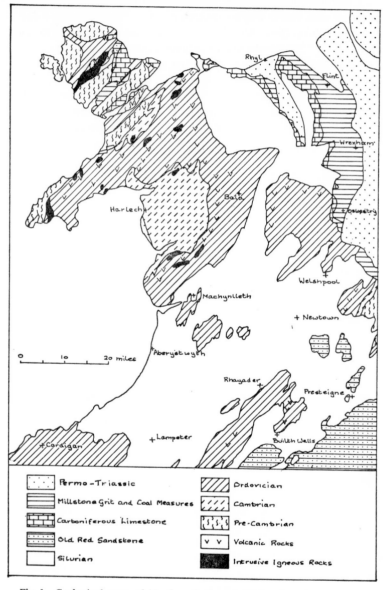

Fig 1   Geological map of North and Central Wales (*based on the work of the Geological Survey and other authors*)

the micro-relief'. Details of the glaciation are treated by Whit-tow and Ball (1970) and by Embleton (1970). The maps are listed in our Bibliography. Mention should also be made of Bassett's invaluable bibliographies and indexes of Welsh geology (1961, 1962-6, 1963, 1967, 1967). It will be realised that North Wales, by reason of its importance, figures largely in the works that deal with the geology of Britain as a whole. The recent Geological Society 'Special Reports' on the correlation of the Cambrian, Ordovician and Silurian rocks of the British Isles are particularly relevant.

CHAPTER 3

The Lleyn Peninsula

In the enchanting distant view of the Lleyn Peninsula from across Cardigan Bay you see the mountain land of Snowdonia stretching out an arm of diminishing hills to the south-west, sinking beneath the sea at the headland of Pen y Cil and re-appearing two miles farther on in the hump and tail of Ynys Enlli, or Bardsey Island.

We shall eventually see that the geology, too, is an extension of the geology of Snowdonia, but the relief in Lleyn has been largely subdued by erosion.

Succession

Silurian	Llandovery
Ordovician	⎧ Upper Bala (Ashgill) ⎪ Lower Bala (Caradoc) ⎨ (?with Llandeilo) ⎪ Llanvirn ⎩ Arenig
Pre-Cambrian	Monian

The western end
Our map, fig 2, shows the geology of the western end of the peninsula. The Pre-Cambrian are the representatives of similar rocks in Anglesey. The volcanic and intrusive igneous rocks are of the Ordovician age.

The Bedded series (or Gwna group) occurs in the far west. It includes sedimentary and volcanic rocks, some of them showing the effects of mild metamorphism. Its most conspicuous member is a *mélange*, a mass of angular fragments of all sizes. This *mélange* poses the question as to whether it is a primary rock-type, perhaps a subaerial landslip deposit, or a gigantic fault-breccia formed during a period of (Pre-Cambrian) thrusting. The

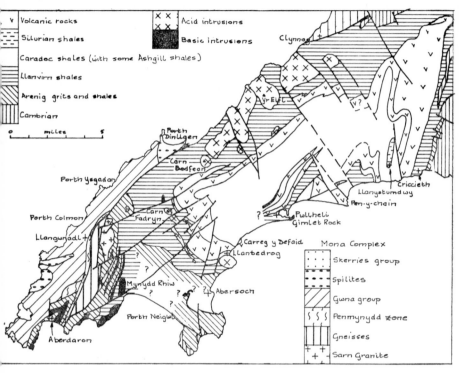

Fig 2 Geological map of the Lleyn Peninsula (*after various authors*)

rocks of the Bedded series are found to be progressively more
and more metamorphosed as they are traced to the south-east,
becoming first schists (Penmynydd zone) and then gneisses.
There is no sharp line of division, all the rocks belong essentially
to the same group (if this interpretation of progressive metamorphism in space is correct).

It is nearly always in sea-cliffs that we find the best rock-
exposures, and here there is a fine series in the little rocky headlands and bays of this north-west-facing coast, which is parallel
to the general alignment of the members of the Bedded series.
To mention a few localities: pillow-lavas are evident in Porth
Dinllaen and the Dinllaen headland, just north of Morfa Nevin;
and the *mélange* at Porth Towyn and Porth Ysgadan, four miles
down the coast, and at Porth Colmon three miles farther on.

Within the Bedded series are basic dykes which are also probably of Pre-Cambrian age.

The Pre-Cambrian rocks, chiefly the *mélange*, re-appear in Bardsey Island and can be seen from a boat in the fine cliffs on the east side of Mynydd Enlli.

About half a mile east of Llangwnadl, exposures of the two successive zones of metamorphism can be seen, schists to the west, gneisses to the east.

Just to the east of the main Pre-Cambrian outcrop, west of the village of Sarn Meyllteyrn, is a granite known as the Sarn Granite. This is certainly pre-Ordovician in age because Ordovician rocks are found lying unconformably on it, and it is assumed to belong to the Pre-Cambrian complex of rocks. The granite is best exposed at the northern end of Myndd Cenamwlch and the critical exposure of the unconformity is seen in Mountain Cottage quarry.

The rocks to the east of the Pre-Cambrian outcrop are of Ordovician age, sedimentary rocks of the Arenig series along the border followed by those of the Llanvirn series. There are contemporaneous lava-flows, both rhyolites and basalts, within these series and intrusions of dolerite sills which are assumed to be also of Ordovician age. These igneous rocks are responsible for the high ground of the headland of Mynydd Penarfynydd and of Mynydd Rhiw to the north. Also the two Gull Islands, Ynys Gwylan, fawr and fach, are composed of parts of a dolerite sill which is continued along a mile of the coast on the mainland.

Manganese ore occurs interbedded in Arenig shales on the southern side of Mynydd Rhiw and near the sea 1½ miles to the south-west. The ore is due to mineralisation of an originally sedimentary rock. These rocks were broken into strips and lenticles by the forces of earth-movement and economic exploitation of the ore is therefore difficult. The last production came during World War II.

The age of these Ordovician strata at this end of the Lleyn Peninsula is of course determined by the fossils, chiefly graptolites. These have been found sporadically and should be looked for wherever there happens to be an exposure at the time. The following have been found: Arenig-age fossils—*Azygograptus, Phyllograptus, Didymograptus hirundo* (an 'extensiform'

species), and the trilobite *'Ogygia' selwyni;* Llanvirn-age fossil—
Didymograptus bifidus (a 'tuning fork' species).

Central Lleyn—sedimentary rocks

Apart from the Pre-Cambrian in the extreme west and the Cambrian in the south of St Tudwal's Peninsula, Lleyn is occupied almost entirely by Ordovician rocks, sedimentaries with igneous extrusions and intrusions. The structure is not very clear but there appears to be a general synclinal arrangement with a slight tilt to the north-east. We find the lowest Ordovician rocks, belonging to the Arenig and Llanvirn series, in the south-west corner as already described. For the rest the rocks are of Bala age; Lower Bala (Caradocian) for the most part, probably including representatives of the Llandeilo series, but also, rather surprisingly for this part of North Wales, there are some beds containing the trilobite *Phillipsinella parabola* which indicates an Upper Bala (Ashgillian) age. These upper beds occur near Crugan, half a mile north of Llanbedrog. More surprising still is the small outcrop of Silurian shales north of Llanystumdwy. Beautiful specimens of graptolites have been found here and the species show that most of the Llandovery series is represented.

Lower Bala fossils may possibly be found wherever these rocks become exposed, such as in new road-cuttings. They include well-known species of brachiopods and trilobites such as those belonging respectively to the *Orthis* family and the *Trinucleus* family. There is also the common problematical little screw-like fossil, *Tentaculites.*

Central Lleyn—igneous rocks

The most interesting part of the geology of the main part of Lleyn is that concerning the igneous rocks, and these provide neat examples of simple geological explanations.

There are three quite distinct facts to be observed about igneous rocks: (1) the size and shape of the outcrops and their relations to the outcrops of the surrounding sedimentary rocks; (2) the mineralogical composition, often conveniently summarised in a chemical sense as being 'acid' or 'basic' (with 'intermediate'); (3) the petrographical texture; that is, whether glassy, microcrystalline (crystals observable only under the microscope), finely crystalline, coarsely crystalline.

Several of these characters usually go together. The large outcrops are either irregular in outline or tend to be somewhat circular or elliptical; they cut across the outcrops of the surrounding sedimentary formations (they are discordant); they are coarse-grained crystalline; the great majority (all those in Wales) are acid, that is, they are granites. From all these facts we infer that these bodies were emplaced deep in the earth's crust and cooled slowly.

The smaller outcrops are usually either circular or elliptical on the one hand, and discordant to the surrounding stratification, or, on the other hand, they occur as elongated strips. The latter are either microcrystalline (sometimes glassy) or finely crystalline giving a speckled appearance to the naked eye. The microcrystalline kinds must have cooled rapidly and are concordant, and as they can be matched with modern lavas it is naturally inferred that they are ancient lavas interbedded in time-sequence with the sedimentary strata; they are extrusions. The finely speckled kinds may be concordant (sills) or discordant (dykes) and it is inferred that these forced their way in a molten state along or across the strata, at no great distance below the earth's surface, cooling fairly rapidly. That is, they are minor intrusions; and this is proved when we find, as we often do, that the sedimentary rocks near the igneous rock have been altered, evidently by heat, commonly having a 'baked' appearance.

All the smaller igneous bodies, extrusive and intrusive, may be either acid or basic in composition. (Briefly, acid igneous rocks are rich, basic relatively poor, in silica, the oxide of silicon.)

In visualising volcanic conditions of the time we can imagine that some at least of the small rather circular outcrops represent the vents of individual volcanoes; they are usually called 'plugs' or 'necks'. The sills, too, are assumed to be associated with the volcanic activity.

The following table shows the various kinds of igneous rock throughout the whole of Lleyn, with mention of a few of the more notable occurrences. There will be more about igneous rocks and volcanism in later sections.

There are a few special points to note. In the first place it is not always possible to distinguish between flows of liquid rhyolitic lava and flows (of similar general composition) of thick

major intrusions	acid (granite)		(Pre-Cambrian) Sarn
minor intrusions	acid (micro-granite)	necks, sills	Carn Fadryn, Mynydd Tir-y-cwmwd, hills from Carn Bodfean to Yr Eifl Nanhoron quarry (Pre-Cambrian) West coast
	basic (dolerite)	dykes, sills	Mynydd Rhiw, north of Pwllheli, Gimlet Rock
extrusions (volcanic)	acid	lava (rhyolite), ash-flow (ignimbrite)	Careg y Defaid, Carn Saethon, Mynydd Rhiw
	basic	lava (basalt)	Mynydd Rhiw

masses of incandescent ash, called a 'nuée ardente' by the French describers of the eruption of Mt Pelée in Martinique in 1902. These latter rocks are called ignimbrites.

Some rocks with texture characteristic of subaerial lava-flows may in fact have been intrusive just below the surface; such rocks have been called 'sub-volcanic' as regards their occurrence.

In referring to the fineness or coarseness of texture we ignore the comparatively large crystals (phenocrysts) that give a porphyritic texture. In these cases it is the ground-mass only that is considered.

The igneous rocks of Lleyn have been extensively quarried. Such rocks, being very hard, are naturally valuable for many constructional and industrial purposes. Quarries in them, particularly when on a large scale, are of the utmost importance to the geologist seeking exposures of the inter-relationships of the various types of igneous rock and the manner of association of the igneous rocks with the surrounding sedimentary rocks. Rocks in general are best seen in two kinds of places: the coast (as already mentioned), where natural erosion produces and lays bare the sea cliffs, and inland quarries where artificial excavation carves far into the rock, making, perhaps, unsightly scars in the landscape but revealing fine rock-surfaces which, near to, may be specially striking when they are fresh, crystalline and sparkling. Very good examples of the latter are to be seen in

Lleyn in those places where the igneous rock is a light-coloured microgranite, and large porphyritic crystals of felspar may add to the beauty of the rock. The largest quarries are those in the hills of Yr Eifl, particularly that south-west of Trefor where the quarry has been cut high into the steep slopes of the northernmost peak of the triple-peaked mountain mass. This peak has been thus artificially accentuated in the acuteness of its seaward profile. Other notable quarries are those on the south side of the headland of Mynydd Tir-y-cwmwd, one mile south of Llanbedrog. This light-coloured microgranite is very distinctive, easily recognisable when it forms, for instance, a component of the beach pebbles on distant coasts such as near Aberystwyth.

There is the quarry in the coarse speckled dolerite of the Gimlet Rock (Carreg yr Imbill), one mile south-east of Pwllheli and near the head of the spit of low ground isolating the harbour from the open sea to the south. Since operations began in 1806 Gimlet Rock has been reduced to a small pinnacle.

Here may be mentioned the great quarries in the igneous rock of Penmaenmawr in the north-east corner of Caernarvonshire. The rock-type does not fit neatly into the usual petrographical classification as it is intermediate in chemical composition between acid and basic and at the same time intermediate in coarseness of grain (it may be called a 'micro-diorite'). These quarries produce the largest output of crushed stone of all igneous-rock quarries in the British Isles. They are also spectacular in that in the main extraction area successive slices are being removed from the crown of the mountain.

In Lleyn the correspondence between outcrop and topography could hardly be more exact. The hard igneous rocks, particularly those of the intrusions, stand up above the surrounding country of less resistant sedimentary rocks, the outlines of their outcrops being accurately delineated by the base of the hills. From a low standpoint at a distance across Cardigan Bay to the south they appear as islands on the horizon. We also see how some of the prominent headlands, such as that at Llanbedrog (and Criccieth to the east) are formed of igneous rock.

The Ice Age
In many British regions of moderate relief a number of features

are due to the activities of the Ice Age. We can list these as follows:

1. A more or less widespread deposit of 'glacial drift', much of it being that most characteristic relic of the Ice Age, boulder-clay.

2. Moraines, found chiefly in the valleys among the mountains.

3. Sands and gravels laid down in temporary lakes ponded back by the ice and in areas traversed by melt-waters.

4. Channels cut either by overflows from the temporary lakes or by streams along the margin of a glacier or ice-sheet (fig 3). These are either now dry or are occupied by only very small streams, the valley being a 'misfit'.

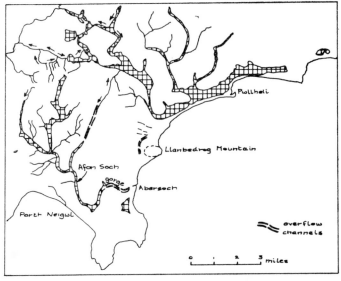

Fig 3 Glacial lakes and overflow channels in the Pwllheli-Abersoch region
(*after Matley, 1936*)

5. Permanent diversions of the pre-glacial drainage. These are caused by the obstruction of the original channels by glacial deposits. They may be local loops or a complete change in the direction of the river. These channels and valleys (items 4 and 5 above) are often steep-sided.

Much of Lleyn is covered with glacial drift and the erratic

boulders, when matched with a 'parent rock', show that this was mostly derived from the ice sheet which passed over Lleyn from the Irish Sea to the north. But there seem also to have been incursions of ice from Snowdonia. As with the 'solid' rocks, the glacial deposits are best seen in cliff sections along the coast as, for instance, in Porth Nevin.

The present Cors Geirch, south-west of Bodfean, was evidently a glacial lake and the sands laid down in it can be examined particularly at Rhyd-y-clafdy at its southern end. The original outlet was probably south-westward through the deep valley of Nant Bodlas, obviously a misfit for its tiny stream. It can be imagined as a possibility that this lake derived its waters from Irish Sea ice still present to the north and was dammed back by ice flowing westward from Snowdonia and having its margin running along a line north-west of Pwllheli and St Tudwal's Peninsula. Another very pronounced and sudden valley, presumably of glacial origin, is that running south-west from Llan-

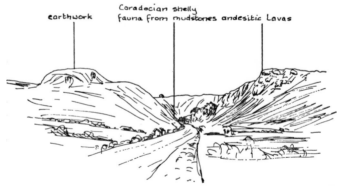

Fig 4   The glacial valley south of Llanbedrog

bedrog (fig 4); but this is at least 'helped' by its having been carved in the softer sedimentary rocks behind the igneous headland of Mynydd Tir-y-cwmwd.

A dramatic case of wholesale glacial diversion is that of the Afon Soch which flows from the north-west to within half a mile of the sea in Hell's Mouth (Porth Neigwl) and then turns back on itself at Llanengan and flows north and east through a deep gorge to Abersoch.

Sources and historical notes
Our detailed knowledge of the geology of Lleyn, apart from St
Tudwal's, is due chiefly to the researches of Matley, occasionally
with a collaborator (1913, 1928, 1930 with Heard, 1932, 1936,
1936 with Smith, 1938). Summaries of previous research are
given in the two more important of these papers (1928, 1938).
Sedgwick and the Geological Survey were the pioneers in the
middle of the last century and the most important of the later
works was Harker's 'Bala volcanic series' (1899) with its detailed
petrographical descriptions. Later researches and statements on
particular areas and problems have been made by Woodland
(1939), Bailey (1954), Shackleton (1954, 1956, 1969), Cattermole
(1969), Tremlett (1969) and Crimes (1970). Some useful indications of localities are to be found in the Geologists' Association
excursion report (Matley and others, 1939). For a full account
of the quarrying of the igneous rocks of North Wales see the
standard work by Thomas (1961); in this work there is also an
account of the manganese mines of the Rhiw district.

c

CHAPTER 4

St Tudwal's

This area provides a very interesting 'geological model' and incidentally is the area where the writer was introduced to field geology, through the kindness of Mr T. C. Nicholas.

Nicholas published a full account of the geology in the *Quarterly Journal* for 1915. This gave the history of previous research, and was supplemented by another, in the same year, on the trilobites. He has also given graphic details in his contribution to the report of the Geologists' Association's excursion in 1939.

He has given the following account of the general geography:

> Towards its south-western extremity Lleyn expands southwards into two promontories, separated by the great bay of Hell's Mouth. The eastern and smaller of these is the St Tudwal's Peninsula.
>
> The district is one of low relief and owing to the general absence of trees it presents a somewhat bare and bleak appearance. The southern part of the peninsula forms a plateau and from this a spur runs northwards to the gorge of the Soch, presenting a bold steep front on the west to the great drift-covered area at the head of Hell's Mouth. This abrupt slope possesses all the characters of an old shore-line continuous with the present one. Most of the country is covered with glacial drift, chiefly in the form of boulder-clay, and is under cultivation; but on Mynydd Cilan coarse glacial gravels give rise to heather-clad ground. Where the solid rocks protrude through the drift they form low knolls and ridges.

Succession

South of the main structural line

Ordovician	Arenig	{ Llanengan Mudstones { Tudwal Sandstones
Cambrian	Upper (Lingula Flags)	{ Ffestiniog beds { Maentwrog beds
	Middle	{ Nant-pig Mudstones { Caered Mudstones and Flags { Cilan Grits
	Lower	{ Mulfran Manganese Mudstones { Hell's Mouth Grits

North of the main structural line

Cambrian and $\left\{\begin{array}{l}\text{Lower Bala}\\\text{Arenig}\\\text{Tremadoc}\end{array}\right\}$ structure confused
Ordovician

Structure

The line of outcrop of a main structural surface crosses the neck of the peninsula (fig 5).

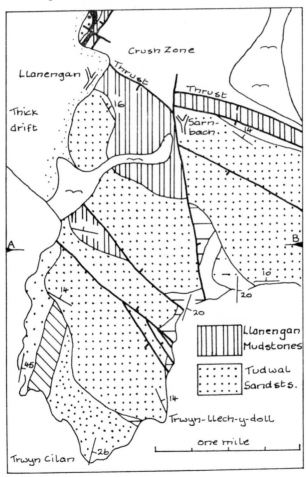

Fig 5 Geological map of the St Tudwal's Peninsula (*after Nicholas, 1915*). Symbols for the Cambrian formations correspond to those in the Harlech Dome (fig 21).

North of this line is a mass of crushed rocks including recognisable representatives of the Tremadoc, Arenig, and Lower Bala series.

South of the line, that is over the greater part of the peninsula, Cambrian rocks (Lower Cambrian to Lingula Flags) with a fairly regular dip of about 20° to the east are overlain unconformably by Ordovician rocks (Lower Arenig) with a dip rather variable in direction and amount but, on the whole, from 10° to 15° to the north-east. The outcrop of this unconformity forms the second of the two main structural lines seen on the map.

Over most of the area the Arenig rocks occur at the surface of the 'solid' structure covering the Cambrian rocks below except where these emerge from beneath the unconformity along parts of the west and south coasts. The unconformity is apparent on the geological map from the way its outcrop cuts across (oversteps) the Cambrian outcrops (see section, fig 6), but it is not so clear in the field because (1) the dips of the two sets of rocks (both being variable) are not very different; and (2) the lithology

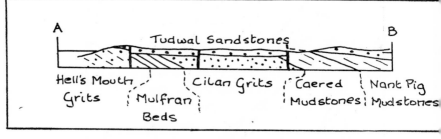

Fig 6   Cross-section through the St Tudwal's Peninsula
(*after Nicholas, 1915*)

of the two sets is rather similar. But there are two places on the cliffs, immediately west of the headland Trwyn Llech-y-doll and on the slopes of Pared Mawr, where the actual juction between the Cambrian and the Arenig rocks is exposed and here the unconformity is beautifully revealed.

The rocks of this main part of the peninsula are traversed by a number of faults which run approximately north-west to south-east. One of these reveals the probable nature of all the faulting. The outcrops of both Cambrian and Arenig lie farther to the south on the west side of this fault than on the east, an arrangement which is most readily explained by supposing the fault to be a (sinistral) tear fault.

Interpretation of these faults as tear faults fits in with the most likely interpretation of the main structural dislocation across the northern part of the peninsula. The outcrop of this dislocation is everywhere parallel to that of the adjacent Lower Arenig beds on its south side, and immediately on its north side beds have been found with graptolites indicating a Lower Bala age. The conclusion from this alone would be that there was a stratigraphical non-sequence here (the Upper Arenig and Llanvirn being absent) representing a time during which no deposits were laid down. But the beds north of the line are, as already mentioned, folded and faulted and crushed in a complicated manner, a state quite different from that of the strata to the south. It therefore seems most likely that the mass of rocks north of the line have been subjected to great pressure from the north and have been thrust southward, over underlying rocks, along a plane whose strike is much the same as the strike of the Lower Arenig. The angular outcrop of this line at and north of Llanengan, together with the observed dips in the underlying Lower Arenig, is evidently the result of the later folding of all these rocks into an anticline north of the village and a syncline just south of the village, the folds plunging to the north-east.

Most of the region is covered by superficial deposits of glacial drift which conceal the rocks below. Thus the map of the 'solid geology' is pieced together from the information given where these rocks are exposed. We have here another good example of the value of coastal erosion in cutting sections across a rock-structure and displaying it along the cliffs.

Hell's Mouth Grits

The general easterly dip of the Cambrian strata brings up the lower groups on the west and so the lowest of these, the Hell's Mouth Grits, outcrops over a strip along the westernmost coast of the peninsula. The beds are continuously exposed along a mile of steep, in places inaccessible, cliffs. The strike of the strata coincides with the trend of the cliffs so that these reveal sections in the same set of beds (figs 7, 8). In the north part of the outcrop the upper beds are concealed beneath the Arenig unconformity,

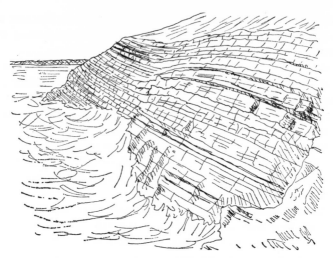

Fig 7   The Hell's Mouth Grits, on the western side of the St Tudwal's
Peninsula (*after Nicholas, 1915*)

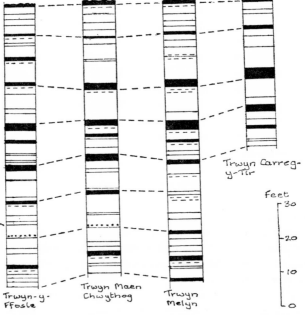

Fig 8   Comparative vertical sections through the Hell's Mouth Grits, on
the western side of the St Tudwal's Peninsula
(*after Bassett and Walton, 1959*)

but elsewhere they pass up into the beds of the Mulfran group.

The Hell's Mouth Grits, as the name implies, have beds of this 'grit' rock-type predominating, with intervening beds of silt-stone and mudstone, and transitions and varieties of all three. The several rock-types alternate in no very regular manner but there is a tendency for a repeated upward sequence of beds of decreasing coarseness, so that coarse grits are followed by finer grits, siltstones, and finally mudstones; the mudstones being followed somewhat abruptly by the coarse grits of the succeeding 'rhythm'. This is an example of a type of sequence that is often found where rocks of this range of grain-size are inter-bedded, and is called 'graded bedding'.

Observed sequences in the lower part of the Hell's Mouth Grits at four points along the coast may be given to show, in the form of geological columns, the vertical alternation of the beds and their lateral variations in thickness (fig 8).

The Hell's Mouth Grits were placed as Lower Cambrian by Nicholas because of their stratigraphical relation to the higher groups whose age was known from the fossils obtained from them. After prolonged search Bassett and Walton made a most important discovery of some fragmentary fossils for the first time. The most significant of these were those of a trilobite which was identified as belonging to the family *Protolenidae*. This is a family which is regarded as establishing the Lower Cambrian age of any rock in which it is found.

Mulfran Manganese Mudstones

The outcrop forms a narrow band east of the Hell's Mouth Grits, emerging at its northern end from beneath the Arenig uncon-formity and in the south truncated by the sea in inaccessible cliffs east of the point Trwyn y Mulfran. The beds are mud-stones with grits, the mudstones containing manganese ore disseminated through them. This results in a peculiar blue-black weathering surface. Similar manganese-bearing beds occur in the Harlech Dome at about the same stratigraphical level. No fossils have been found.

Cilan Grits

Following above the Mulfran beds this group, about 1,000ft thick, is exposed in the cliffs around Trwyn Cilan at the southern tip of the peninsula. Massive grits make up most of the total thickness. No fossils have been found.

Caered Mudstones and Flags

All the exposures of these beds occur in the cliffs of the bay from which they take their name. The lowest beds may be seen in the little indentation west of Trwyn Llech-y-doll (fig 9). Here

Fig 9   The Arenig unconformity at Trwyn Llech-y-doll
(after Nicholas, 1915)

there is a passage up from the Cilan Grits and the beds are cut off above by the Arenig unconformity. The main exposure of the group is along the north-west part of the curve of Porth Caered, where there is an upward sequence from south-west to north-east. Flags are followed by mudstones of the upper part of the group which are very well shown in the cliff of Pared Mawr. These mudstones are fossiliferous, the fossils being mainly of the very small trilobite genera *Agnostus* (particularly the species *A. fissus*) and *Eodiscus* (the well-known species *E. punctatus*). The much larger *Paradoxides hicksi* also occurs. All these trilobite forms are characteristic of the Middle Cambrian. The horny brachiopod *Lingulella* is also common.

Nant-pig Mudstones

This group has a small thickness and a small outcrop in the cliffs but is specially interesting because it is very fossiliferous, more so even than the Caered mudstones. Again, species of *Agnostus*, together with *Eodiscus punctatus*, are the chief forms. The best collecting locality so far found is at a rather precipitous spot near the top of the cliff.

Maentwrog beds
The Nant-pig Mudstones are suddenly succeeded by beds with a lithology typical of the Lingula Flags of North Wales and especially typical of the lowest of the three divisions, the Maentwrog series. The flags are hard fine-textured pale micaceous sandstones from a few inches to about a foot or two in thickness. They are a sharp contrast, in colour and hardness, to the dark soft intervening mudstones and stand out prominently on the weathered surfaces of the cliffs. The weathered surfaces of these 'ringers' usually show curled and contorted primary bedding. Much of the outcrop is obscured by a thick mass of scree covered with glacial drift. Only a few fragments of fossils have been found, these being of the trilobites *Agnostus pisiformis* and *Olenus*.

Ffestiniog beds
The south-eastern half of St Tudwal's Island East is occupied by a series of rocks the lithology of which strongly recalls the Ffestiniog division (the middle division) of the Lingula Flags. This is confirmed by the occurrence, in the uppermost beds exposed, of a bed crowded with the brachiopod *Lingulella davisi*. This is no doubt to be correlated with the well-known Lingulella Band which generally occurs elsewhere in North Wales at the top of the Ffestiniog series.

Tudwal Sandstones
This formation occupies about two-thirds of the total area of the peninsula and islands so it has been named after the peninsula itself. The most extensive section is along the cliffs of Penrhyn Du on the east, but the general characteristics are well displayed and most easily seen in the fine cliff which runs out to the headland of Trwyn Wylfa. It is, however, difficult to make out any definite succession of beds within the group, partly because the standstone lithology is much the same throughout and partly because there are faults which confuse the structure.

At the base of the Tudwal Sandstones series, immediately where it overlies the unconformity, there is (as usual in such cases) a thin layer of conglomeratic rock representing the pebbly deposit laid down as the sea advanced across the old land surface. The pebbles are chiefly rock-types to be found in the Pre-Cambrian Monian. Some are encrusted with the problematical organism *Bolopora undosa* which is a curious characteristic of the basal Arenig conglomerate elsewhere in North Wales.

Fossils within the group are sparse but have been found in the shales which occur interbedded with the sandstones, especially where they are quarried at inland localities such as Sarn-bach, exposing weathered surfaces. These fossils are extensiform graptolites characteristic of the lower part of the Arenig series: *Didymograptus deflexus* and *D. extensus*, the former being the commoner. Dendroid graptolites have also been found.

At the top of this group are 30ft of beds which, while being 'passage beds' into the succeeding Llanengan Mudstones, are nevertheless easily recognisable by the colour and texture of the sandstones with their numerous thin mudstone intercalations. These mudstones have yielded some well-preserved specimens of the curious 'one-armed' extensiform graptolite, *Azygograptus lapworthi*, another characteristic Lower Arenig fossil. The distinctive character of these passage beds has allowed them to be mapped right across the peninsula.

Llanengan Mudstones

This group outcrops over more or less separated areas in the west and north. Graptolites, *Azygograptus lapworthi* and, rarely *Tetragraptus* occur, still indicating beds in the lower part of the Arenig series.

Rocks north of the overthrust

The rocks north (and north-east) of the overthrust, that is, overlying this thrust-surface, have a very complicated structure: over most of the area the order of succession of the beds is unclear, nor do the rocks give an indication of their age.

Around the headland of Pen Benar, just east of Abersoch where there are continuous exposures to be viewed in the low cliffs, the complex structure is exemplified. Moreover, fossils are found here at several spots, particularly the dendroid grap-

tolite *Dictyonema flabelliforne* indicating the well-known Dictyonema Band in the lower part of the (Cambrian) Tremadoc
series of North Wales and *Azygograptus lapworthi* and *Tetragraptus* of the (Ordovician) Arenig. Parts of the structure can
thus be fixed as regards their ages, and correlated. This is shown
in the map and section (fig 10).

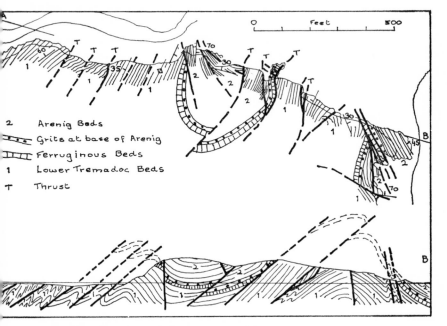

Fig 10   Geological map and cross section of Pen Benar, Abersoch
(after Nicholas, 1915)

Again in the south-west of this northern part of the peninsula, in the neighbourhood of Llanengan, graptolites indicating
a Lower Bala age occur in shales associated with masses of
pisolitic iron ore. These beds have been quarried, particularly at
Hen-dy-capel and Pen-y-gaer where the best exposures have been
artificially created. The iron ore seems to take its place as an
altered sedimentary rock lying at the base of the whole series
of crushed rocks.

Igneous rocks
There are a few small dolerite sills in the north-west corner of

the area in the neighbourhood of Llanengan and Peny-y-gaer. These are emplaced among both the Arenig rocks and those of the crushed area. They must of course be later in age than the formation of the newest rocks into which they are intruded, assuming all the intrusions to have occurred at the same time. They also appear to be later than the crushing of the rocks because crushed shales close to the dolerite have been 'baked' white by the hot intruding magma. But as they take part in the general folding of the rocks here they must have been intruded before this folding occurred.

CHAPTER 5

Arvon and the Llanberis Slate Belt

Arvon is that part of Caernarvonshire which lies opposite Anglesey, extending inland from the Menai Strait to the foothills of Snowdonia (fig 11).

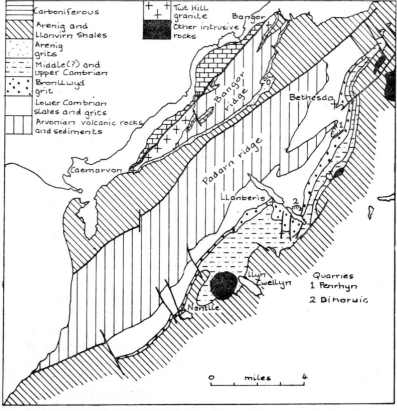

Fig 11   Geological map of the Slate Belt and the lowlands of Arvon
(*after various authors*)

A number of interesting problems arise here which give us the opportunity of looking into the heart of geology, that is, into the 'explanations' of what we see.

The rock formations present in the area belong to the Cambrian, Ordovician, and Carboniferous sytems; but the lowest of those here included in the Cambrian, the Arvonian, has usually been placed as Pre-Cambrian. There are many gaps in the succession.

Succession

Carboniferous

Ordovician   Arenig

Cambrian
$\left\{\begin{array}{l} \text{Upper} \\ \text{(Lingula Flags)} \\ \\ \text{Lower} \end{array}\right.$
$\left\{\begin{array}{l} \text{Ffestiniog beds} \\ \text{Maentwrog beds} \\ \text{Llanberis Slates} \\ \text{Conglomerate and grits} \\ \text{Arvonian} \end{array}\right.$

Arvonian

There are the two outcrops, known as the Bangor Ridge and the Padarn Ridge. The rocks are all igneous and, except for a granite at the south-west end of the Bangor Ridge, all volcanic. These volcanic rocks have until recently been described as mostly rhyolitic lavas and tuffs but, as in the case of the much later Snowdonian volcanics, are now interpreted (particularly in the Padarn Ridge) as being largely ignimbrites.

Presumably the rocks of the two outcrops are connected not very deeply underground, the part between them being overlain unconformably by the Ordovician (and, in addition, being heavily drift-covered). The rocks of the Padarn Ridge are said by some authorities to form an anticline, but the evidence for such a structure is not clear.

The following are some of the places where the Arvonian rocks of the Bangor Ridge (which stretches from Bangor to Caernarvon) may be studied: Twt Hill, Caernarvon, in which the granite appears at the south-west end of its outcrop; Port Dinorwic, where the granite at the north-east end of its outcrop is visible, and where there is an escarpment of the volcanic rocks to the south-east of the main road; 'Bangor Mountain', where there are rugged outcrops of volcanic rocks overlooking the east side of the city.

The Arvonian rocks of the Padarn Ridge are to be seen in several places about Llyn Padarn. There are good exposures at the village of Cwm-y-glo, three-quarters of a mile north-west of the outlet of the lake. However, it is the exposures on the north of the eastern end of the lake that have been examined for over a hundred years in the controversy, still very much alive, as to the relation between the Arvonian and the overlying rocks. This area has been re-mapped recently by D. Wood.

Lower Cambrian
Following the Arvonian on the south-east side of the Padarn Ridge outcrop is a succession of Cambrian formations dipping to the south-east. There is first a conglomerate followed by grits, both together being about 2,000ft thick. Much has been made in the past of a supposed unconformity at the base of the conglomerate, but the evidence all seems to indicate a conformable passage of the Arvonian up into the sedimentary rocks. The passage is a gradual one, with volcanic and sedimentary layers interbedded.

Following the grits are the Llanberis Slates, about 2,500ft thick. Towards the top a few fossils have been found, particularly the trilobite *Pseudatops viola* (formerly known as *Conocoryphe viola*), which are taken to indicate a (rather late?) Lower Cambrian age. The fossil is described and the finds up to 1950 are discussed by Howell and Stubblefield, and a few further trilobite specimens have been found by Wood. The whole of the Llanberis Slates formation and the underlying grits formation are thus assigned to the Lower Cambrian.

The following remarks about the slates of North Wales in general and those of Caernarvonshire in particular are mostly taken from Thomas's article on 'Wales: land of mines and quarries' which itself is largely based on North's standard book *The slates of Wales*. See also Thomas's important work *The mineral wealth of Wales*.

The Cambrian slate belt of north-western Caernarvonshire, containing the famous Penrhyn (Bethesda) and Dinorwic (Llanberis quarries, is relatively narrow and ranges southwestward for about eleven miles from Betheseda to Nantlle and Penygroes. There are several beds or 'veins' of workable slate with indifferent slates or sandy beds between them. Most of the slates are

Fig 12   The Dinorwic slate quarries at Llanberis, viewed from across Llyn Peris (*after North, 1946*)

reddish-purple or blue in colour but some of the upper 'veins' are green. The most important Ordovician outcrop is that which traverses, likewise in a southwesterly direction, the Blaenau-Ffestiniog area. Here the slates are on the whole finer in grain and mainly blue in colour; most of them have been extracted by mining rather than from open quarries. In the Corris area and in the adjoining parts of southern Merioneth and western Montgomeryshire, two important slate 'veins' have been extensively mined and quarried.

Slate was known and used for roofing in Roman times, though the workings probably amounted only to scratchings of the more obvious outcrops to obtain material for local use. The Industrial Revolution and the associated rapid growth of population and improvement of transport facilities led to the general adoption of slate as a roofing material. Before the introduction of railways, slate for distant markets was transported by sea through ports developed specifically for this purpose: Port Penrhyn for Penrhyn quarry, Port Dinorwic for Dinorwic quarry, Caernarvon for the Nantlle quarries, Portmadoc for Blaenau-Ffestiniog, and Aberdovey for southern Merioneth. Most of the branch lines of the railway system in this part of north-western Wales were routed through or from slate-quarrying areas.

Inclination of the slate 'veins' (which are bedding units) largely determines the methods of working. Where dips are almost vertical, individual slate beds can be followed downward by means of deep pits, as in the Nantlle valley, or in more mountainous areas can be worked from a series of terraces or galleries cut into the hillside, as in the huge Dinorwic and Penrhyn quarries. If the beds are inclined at rather low angles, quarrying would soon encounter unmanageable amounts of overlying

cleavage

bedding

Fig 13   *Splitting large blocks in a slate quarry (after North, 1946)*

waste rock. In such places mining is resorted to, as in the Blaenau-Ffestiniog area, in other parts of Merioneth, and in eastern Caernarvonshire. Mining, however, though it does not necessitate removal of overlying rock, wastes some 40 to 50 per cent of the good slate, which must be left in stout pillars for roof support.

The 'age' of a rock

An important question arises as to the senses in which we should

D

speak of the 'age' of such rocks as the Llanberis Slates. In the stratigraphical sense they are 'Lower Cambrian'. But the age of the rocks as they now are, as slates, is post-Silurian, probably early Devonian. If the slates were merely mechanically deformed mudstones the question would hardly arise; but there is mineralogical change, the rocks are metamorphic rocks, though of a low grade of metamorphism. A little more metamorphism and they might be schists, and the 'age' of a schist-formation, as such, is the age of the metamorphism which produced the new schist rock, though no doubt we should be concerned to know its previous history before the transformation.

The age of an ordinary sandstone formation, for instance, is the age of its deposition, not the age of a granite from which its (quartz) grains were no doubt ultimately derived. The age of a granite is the age of its consolidation from a melt (magma); a melt, perhaps, of previously existing rocks.

The stratigraphical status of the Arvonion—'Cambrian' and 'Pre-Cambrian'

A question of fundamental importance arises as to the placing of the Arvonian on the stratigraphical scale, namely whether it is possible to recognise a general stratigraphical (time) boundary between the Cambrian and the Pre-Cambrian. It is a matter of a failure in the 'fossil record'.

The fossil record, on being traced downwards through the rocks, cannot be expected to come to an end everywhere at the same stratigraphical level. Here, near the top of the Llanberis Slates, we have fossils indicating a high Lower Cambrian horizon, but there are none in any part of the apparently conformably underlying rocks, some of which at least must be presumed to be in a lower part of the Lower Cambrian. There is a very thick sequence of these lower rocks (including the Arvonian); are they all 'Cambrian' or, if we are going to call some of them 'Pre-Cambrian', where should the base of the Cambrian be drawn?

The important thing to realise is that there are no lithological or structural facts that enable one to say from positive evidence in any region, 'this is Pre-Cambrian'. Absence of fossils in stratigraphically very low-lying rocks such as we have here merely indicates that they may be. It is possible that, in the future, radiometric methods may help in establishing an agreed general base to the Cambrian system, a stratigraphical (time) level which would of course be also the top of the Pre-Cambrian.

Across the straits, in Anglesey, and in south-western Lleyn, there are the Monian rocks. This is such a vast collection of metamorphic rocks, so different from the rocks of the rest of our region, that at least we must treat them separately. The Geological Survey of last century took them to be metamorphosed Cambrian. They are certainly older than the Ordovician because rocks of that age overlie them unconformably; and there is no intervening Cambrian recognisable by its fossils. The Monian formation (or, rather, collection of formations) is now taken as Pre-Cambrian by all authorities.

This arrangement, with the Arvonian placed with the Cambrian and the Monian relegated to a Pre-Cambrian era, goes back to the original assignment of Sedgwick in the 1830s and later. It was Sedgwick who founded the Cambrian system and gave it that name, and he included in it all the rocks as far north-westwards as the Menai Strait, that is, all the rocks later known as the Arvonian. The present writer has recently discussed this question in detail.

Cambrian above the Lower Cambrian
Above the Llanberis Slates come about 1,000ft of grits, the Bronllwyd Grits, then another formation of slaty rocks, and then beds which again, at last, contain fossils, showing them to belong to the Ffestiniog series. The underlying slaty rocks pass up conformably into these Ffestiniog beds and both for this reason and because of their lithological similarity to the Maentwrog beds in general they are placed as belonging to the Maentwrog series.

The Bronllwyd Grits have been tentatively correlated in various ways by various authorities, but it is usually assumed that they represent the lower part of the Maentwrog series, a part (called the Vigra Grits) which is more arenaceous than the rest of the series. On this view the Middle Cambrian is missing and there must be a non-sequence between the Llanberis Slates and the Bronllwyd Grits.

There are no further representatives of the Cambrian system —no Dolgelley beds nor Tremadoc series. Above the Ffestiniog beds come the beds of the Arenig series of the Ordovician, and here the non-sequence may be, rather, a structural unconformity.

The doubts about the mutual relations and the equivalents elsewhere of the Cambrian formations in this area are due to the scarcity of fossils, and thus we see how essential these are in the study of the stratigraphy of a region.

Ordovician of the Bangor-Caernarvon district
The Ordovician rocks in the neighbourhood of the Bangor-Caernarvon outcrop contain fossils characteristic of the Arenig and the lower part of the Llanvirn series, that is belonging to the three zones, *Didymograptus extensus*, *D. hirundo*, and *D. bifidus*. The two most notable sections where fossils may be obtained are those along the left bank of the Afon Seiont at Caernarvon described by Gertrude Elles, and a little exposure along the shore betwen the two great Menai bridges described by Greenly. At Llandegai, one mile south-east of Bangor, the sedimentary rock is in the form of a pisolitic iron ore.

The unconformity between the base of the Ordovician and the underlying rocks in the Bangor-Caernarvon area is revealed by the mapping and by the fact that there are no (undoubted) Cambrian rocks between the Ordovician and the Arvonian. Greenly mentions a point 170yd west of Bangor pier where the unconformity seemed to be actually visible.

Carboniferous
Finally, the Carboniferous rocks are present on the Menai Strait side of the Bangor Arvonian ridge and are described in Chapter 12. The line of unconformity at their base is essentially transgressive across the outcrop of the unconformity between the Ordovician and Arvonian, but by chance it happens to follow it rather closely. Incidentally, the comparison of Greenly's two 'solid' maps of 1944 with his 'drift' map of 1941 suggests that the lines on the 'solid' maps must be largely conjectural. When you visit the ground you will be impressed by the difficulties of geological mapping!

Sources and further historical notes
Following the pioneer work of Sedgwick, already referred to,

there came the detailed and remarkably accurate work of the Geological Survey under Ramsay (one-inch maps, 1852; Memoir, 1866 and 1881). The important paper by Gertrude Elles on the graptolite zones of the Arenig and Llanvirn series exposed in the river Seiont near Caernarvon was published in 1904.

The only detailed account of a succession within the Llanberis Slates formation is that at Nantlle by Morris and Fearnsides (1926).

Modern research on the Arvonian and associated rocks of the Arvon region was carried out by Greenly, his two most important papers being those in the *Quarterly Journal* for 1944. He was assisted by D. Williams, whose later independent work remains unpublished. The essay by D. Wood (1969) embodies important details concerning, in particular, the nature of the Arvonian-Llanberis Slates boundary. The *Slates of Wales* (1925, 1946), one of North's series of invaluable handbooks, and Thomas's works (1955, 1961) have been referred to in the text.

CHAPTER 6

Central Snowdonia

Snowdon and its surrounding mountains provide the splendid centrepiece to the scenic grandeur of North Wales. Here too the geology is extremely spectacular and most obviously invites minute examination and broad interpretation. What kinds of rocks are these mountains made of; how were these rocks formed; in what geological period; and what were the geographical conditions at the time in this region of the earth's surface that we know as 'North Wales'? How did the mountains originate and how have they come to be as they are? What evidence is there of the most recent events in geological and physiographical history?

Succession at Snowdon

Ordovician	⎧ Lower Bala (Caradoc) ⎪ (?with Llandeilo) ⎨ ⎪ Llanvirn ⎩ Arenig	⎧ Snowdon Volcanic series ⎨ Gwastadnant Grits ⎩ Glanrafon Slates Maesgwm Slates Plas-y-nant beds
Cambrian	Upper (Lingula Flags)	

The question as to whether there are any representatives of 'Llandeilo' rocks is a little technical but had better be explained. It is a twofold matter:

(1) Up to about thirty or forty years ago the general Llandeilo series always included three graptolite zones, but latterly only the lowest of these, that of *Glyptograptus teretiusculus*, has been assigned to the Llandeilo, the other two being removed into the Caradocian. In Snowdonia the upper two zones are represented; in the older literature these are therefore classed as 'Llandeilo' but in the newer they are classed with the Caradocian.

(2) Rocks representing the present, restricted, 'Llandeilo' have

not been certainly found in Snowdonia. Either (a) they are really absent, there being a non-sequence, perhaps with some structural unconformity, or (b) the lowest beds of the Glanrafon series belong to the zone though its characteristic graptolites have not been certainly identified.

Although the Snowdon Volcanic series keeps something of its identity beyond the immediate neighbourhood of that mountain itself, there is much variation in the Ordovician formations below. For instance, the Gwastadnant Grits at Snowdon become merged with the Glanrafon Slates elsewhere, while there is in places a volcanic series intercalated near the base of the Glanrafon series.

Structure
The rock-formations of practically the whole of Caernarvonshire, and particularly the main, central, part with which we are here concerned, are arranged in the form of a synclinorium with a general north-east to south-west fold-alignment (fig 14). On the north-west are the Arvonian rocks followed inwards (south-eastwards) by the Cambrian, while on the south-east are the Cambrian rocks of the Harlech Dome. The main part of the synclinorium is occupied by Ordovician rocks from the Arenig to the Lower Bala (=Caradocian) series.

The detailed structure of this Ordovician part is very complicated (fig 15). 'The whole country may be likened to a set of crumpled sheets of paper, to the folds of which a general but irregular direction has been given, and in which some of the larger trough-shaped folds are interfered with, and die out, in consequence of the appearance of other anticlinal and synclinal curves.' This was written by Andrew Ramsay as long ago as 1866 and remains the perfect description of the general structural state. There is no one dominant synclinal line running along the middle of the whole structure. The individual more or less boat-shaped folds tend to be arranged in echelon. The whole structure is further complicated by some of these, and particularly one of the largest, the Dolwyddelan Syncline, being out of alignment with the regional trend. The smaller folds are beautifully displayed on the mountain flanks, notably the synclines of Cwm Idwal (fig 16) and Clogwyn Du'r Arddu, the bold anticlinal curve between Tryfan (fig 17) and Gallt-yr-ogof, and

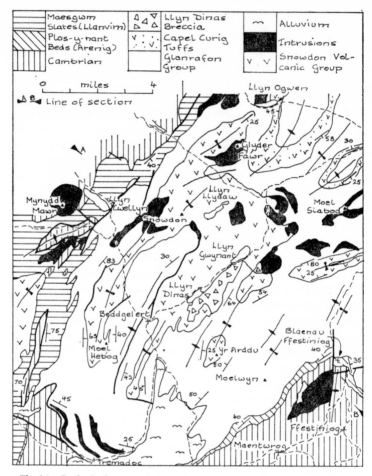

Fig 14   Geological map of Central Snowdonia (*after several authors*)

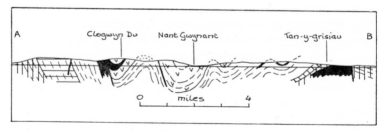

Fig 15   Cross-section through Central Snowdonia

Fig 16 The Cwm Idwal syncline

the syncline visible on the precipice below the summit of Snowdon itself. This general folding simultanously impressed on the more susceptible (the finer-grained) rocks a steeply inclined cleavage more or less parallel to the axial planes of the folds.

Fig 17 Tryfan from the south-east

Volcanicity and associated igneous action
The volcanic rocks exposed in the Snowdon mountains indicate the volcanicity of a long-past geological age. We have seen

something of this in Lleyn and we have already sorted out the different kinds of volcanic rocks and intrusive rocks associated with them. Just as the fold-structures are to be seen so dramatically in the mountain walls of Snowdonia, so too are the volcanic rocks, interbedded with the sedimentary rocks.

In case any reader should not yet realise quite clearly what is meant by such a phrase as 'the old volcanoes of Snowdonia' let it be firmly said that the 'old volcanoes' no longer exist, and that Snowdon, for instance, is certainly not an old volcano; neither the mountain itself nor its peaks and hollows are the relics of any old volcano. Snowdon and its fellow mountains have been carved out of a thick spread of rocks, sedimentary and volcanic, the former entirely and the latter at least partly laid down in the sea, some 450 million years ago, and these rocks have subsequently been upraised to form a high land. The volcanoes themselves very soon vanished leaving no trace. If they lasted as hills, many of them probably conical islands, for a few thousand years, what is that compared with all the millions that have passed since? It is a different matter that we can sometimes see, cut across on the present land-surface, the lower part of a volcanic 'neck' or 'pipe' through which lava welled up to the surface, as mentioned in our account of Lleyn.

The main object of the geologist in studying these old volcanic and associated intrusive rocks here in Snowdonia (as elsewhere) is to reconstruct the geography and conditions of the time, and the igneous processes involved. To do that we naturally want to know exactly what is happening in regions of present-day volcanic activity. In turn, we should learn much from the study of the old igneous rocks, which in many respects reveal more today than could have been seen at the time, and thus show what is happening now, though underground and invisible.

In an article on the 'Ordovician Volcanoes of North Wales' in *Nature in Wales* for 1960, Nicholas Rast has given a very clear and concise account of the main features of volcanic activity that are of particular interest from the geological point of view. We quote his account below:

> A modern volcano normally involves a vertical pipe through which molten rock material (magma) gains admission to the surface of the earth. The pipe is opened and enlarged partly by explosion and partly as a result of the power of the magma to tear away and enclose the surrounding solid country rocks. Thus, a verti-

cal column of magma pierces the crust and reaches the outer surface of the earth, where the magma is disgorged on to the surrounding land or sea-bed, forming flows of molten lava. This lava cools and consolidates and is transformed into volcanic rock, which is usually fine-grained and massive, and may be partly glassy and partly crystalline. The lavas may be relatively rich in iron, magnesium and calcium, when they are known as basic, or in silicon, sodium and potassium, when they are known as acid. Thus, the terms acid and basic are not used in a normal chemical sense. There are also lavas intermediate in character between basic and acid, but for our purpose [the consideration of the Ordovician volcanoes of North Wales] such are relatively unimportant. All lavas also contain some dissolved gases such as water vapour and carbon dioxide. Basic lavas are relatively mobile and from these the gases escape easily and fairly quietly. If, however, the lava is acid it is relatively viscous and the gases tend to accumulate in pockets, where pressure rises producing explosions. Explosions are also common in the original volcanic centre before such lava is erupted. In volcanoes involving acid and intermediate magmas the relatively stiff, but molten, magma is torn into small globules or larger masses which are flung into the atmosphere, where they are rapidly cooled and drop around the volcanic orifice producing a circular mound around the central crater. At the same time some of the solid wall-rock is also brecciated, contributing to the contents of the mound, which soon achieves a conical form and is known as an 'ash cone', although the volcanic ash which forms it is not ash in a conventional sense since it is a product of explosion rather than of burning. In the immediate proximity of the crater much of the fragmentary material is very coarse, with the constituent fragments being the size of a boulder or even bigger. Such a deposit is known as agglomerate.

Collectively the fragmentary products of volcanic eruptions are known as pyroclastic. Thus, the two main products of vulcanicity are the effusive lavas and the pyroclastic ashes (tuffs when consolidated) and agglomerates. Amongst the modern volcanoes those involving the mobile basic magma have little associated pyroclastic material but many extensive lava flows. The bulk of the Welsh Ordovician volcanic deposits are acid.

Modern volcanoes which exude acid magma produce much ash and agglomerate but no extensive lava-flows, and even the latter show a considerable amount of internal disruption and fragmentation (autobrecciation) produced as a result of explosive activity of the gases during the flowage of the very stiff lava. Moreover, in addition to the effusion of lavas or the evolution of rising clouds of fragments, acid eruptions result in the emission of incandescent clouds moving at high speeds close to the ground surface. Such clouds have been called 'nuées ardentes' on the island of Martinique where a whole town (St Pierre) was devastated in 1902 by one of them. Once a nuée ardente comes to rest a chaotic mixture of incandescent particles and fragments settles in a thick sheet. However, unlike normal pyroclastic ashes the deposits of a nuée ardente maintain their internal heat for a considerable time. Moreover, while normal volcanic ash settles particle by particle, resulting in the production of stratification and layering which is especially pronounced in water-laid ashes, the particles in a *nuée ardente* all settle together. Thus these deposits may become agglutinated and it has been suggested that this process implies softening and welding of the particles together. All the deposits of *nuées ardentes* are called 'ignimbrites'.

The kinds and ages of the igneous rocks

The great majority of the igneous rocks of Snowdonia belong to the following groups:

Ignimbrite. Most of the purely igneous volcanic acid rocks are now established as being ignimbrites, formed under subaerial conditions, that is laid down on the land. These were formerly classed as rhyolitic lavas, laid down in the sea.

Bedded pyroclastic. Stratified pyroclastic deposits interbedded with fossiliferous sediments; all laid down in the sea.

Rhyolitic 'plugs', probably representing the smaller volcanic vents.

Microgranite (in a wide sense) in outcrops of varying size, probably representing the larger volcanic vents.

Dolerite sills.

The ignimbrites and the bedded pyroclastic rocks take their places in the stratigraphical sequence. The main developments are in the Snowdon Volcanic series and this has long been divided thus:

> *Upper Rhyolitic series*
> *Bedded Pyroclastic series*
> *Lower Rhyolitic series.*

As a result of the most recent discrimination of rock-types the two 'Rhyolitic series' should probably be called the 'Ignimbrite series'.

Volcanicity began in earliest Caradocian times and ignimbrites are found in the lowest Glanrafon beds.

Ages of intrusions must always be less certainly known than the ages of interstratified extrusions. That the microgranites are intrusions is known primarily by their cross-cutting relations to the stratified and associated volcanic rocks. For the microgranites this is confirmed by the petrographical character, as the crystalline texture could only have resulted from relatively slow cooling below the earth's surface. This last criterion applies also to the dolerites. The intrusive nature of the microgranites and dolerites is further confirmed by the fact that they have produced metamorphism in the adjacent rocks.

The igneous instrusions in North Wales are all into rocks of Ordovician (or earlier) age, therefore there is no evidence that any of them must be of Silurian or later date. Evidence that the microgranite intrusions are earlier than the period of deformation at the end of Silurian times is provided by the cleavage that was produced at that period. In places, metamorphic 'spots' have been found to have been affected by the cleavage, and whereas the intrusions cut across the bedding the cleavage is deflected round the intrusions.

The dolerite sills are closely related to the volcanic rocks and take part in the folding.

Thus it is evident that all the igneous rocks here are the products of one period of igneous activity, the Lower Bala (Caradocian) period. The microgranites probably represent the sites of the larger volcanic eruptions.

The relation between the igneous activity and the development of the structure

The main folding, faulting, and cleavage are the three expressions of the deformation produced at the end of Silurian times, and are the result of lateral (tangential) pressures in the earth's crust. But there would probably be some movement associated with the Ordovician igneous activity, and the recognition of the alternation of subaerial and marine conditions over particular areas shows that there must have been an oscillation of the crustal surface. We may envisage warping with, perhaps, faulting, resulting in more or less vertical movements. These would be very slight compared with the later tremendous compressions and upheavals. Nevertheless, some existing structural features may be due to contemporary (Ordovician) movements associated with the local volcanic and sub-volcanic action. The present arrangement of the stratification and structure would also be complicated as a result of slight unconformities, or at least non-sequences, produced by the alternation of land and sea conditions.

Glaciation

Snowdonia provides magnificent examples of the scenic effects brought about by the action of ice during the Ice Age.

We can visualise the geography of North Wales, at the onset of the glacial conditions, as being very much as it is at the present day in the course of its coastline and the dispositions and heights of the hills.

The mountains of North Wales were snow-covered; glaciers descended the valleys and, splaying out on the lowland plains, coalesced to form continuous sheets of ice. From several major centres of dispersion the ice flowed in a general radial direction, eastwards to the Shropshire-Cheshire plain, northwards into the Irish Sea, westwards into Cardigan Bay and St George's Channel.

At the same time, ice flows from south-west Scotland, northeast Ireland, and the English Lake District converged onto the Irish Sea. From this area of congestion the combined flows moved southwards, part being driven against the land mass of North-Wales. This Irish Sea ice met the front of the Welsh mountains and the northward-flowing ice from Snowdonia, and a part of it was diverted south-westwards and flowed across Anglesey and the Menai region onto and across the Lleyn Peninsula into Cardigan Bay.

The extensions of the Irish Sea ice upon the land surface are nowadays indicated by the occurrence of rocks derived from the north. There also occur at various heights on the hill-slopes many patches of sand containing marine shells which were obviously dredged up from the sea-floor to the north. The most famous instance of this is at nearly 1,400ft on Moel Tryfan between Caernarvon and Snowdon.

The topography of the land-surface and the rocks themselves now show the effects of glacial erosion. Outcrops of rock have been smoothed to form *roches moutonnées* with grooves and scratches still plainly visible. Amphitheatres with very steep rocky walls ('cirques', 'corries'), the chief feeding-grounds of mountain glaciers, constitute a major element in the scenic grandeur of the mountains (fig 18). Many of these contain small lakes. The serrated knife-edges, sharp summits, and pinnacled crags are all related features. Most of the glaciers were powerful enough to produce a characteristic U-shaped profile (fig 19), and in places the irregularly eroded valley floors have been hollowed into rock basins, now occupied by elongate lakes.

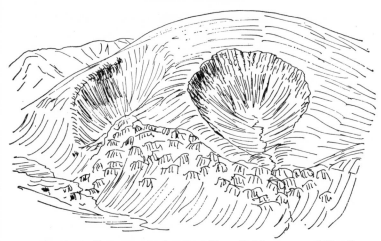

Fig 18   A diagrammatic sketch of Mynydd Mawr, east of Nantlle
(*after Davis, 1909*)

Fig 19   The U-shaped valley of Nant Ffrancon
(*after Smith and George, 1960*)

On the final departure of the ice, extensive deposits of boulder-clay, glacial sands, and moraines were left behind. Some of these formed barriers, holding up lakes: it is not clear, in most cases, to what extent such lakes (in the valleys and the cirques) may be due also to the actual excavation of hollows by the ice.

The above summary is almost entirely selected from the comprehensive yet concise general account given by George in the
Regional Geology handbook. Examples of the effects of ice action
are to be found in innumerable localities.

The origin and evolution of the mountains
The diversity of ideas about the origin and evolution of the
present mountains of North Wales was well shown at a meeting
of the Geological Society of London on 3 November 1937 when
a paper by Edward Greenly was read on 'The age of the mountains of Snowdonia' (published in 1938) and discussed by some
of the most eminent geologists of the day. This diversity of ideas
still remains.

There is one question that needs looking into carefully as its
resolution affects the very core of geomorphology. It comes up
urgently for consideration here, but it is a very general question which arises whenever the history of the relief of an upland
or mountainous area is considered.

When we view the Snowdon mountain-group from any point
outside, for instance from Anglesey, we can imagine a line
connecting the higher summits, and we see that this line is a

Fig 20   The mountains of Snowdonia seen from eastern Anglesey

fairly even one (fig 20). Combining several such views we find
that the summits reach a gently convex imaginary 'hill-top surface'. This is also evident from a map showing the relief and the
heights of the hills.

It may at first sight be tempting to suggest that this imaginary hill-top surface coincides with a once-real surface of a dome-shaped mass out of which the mountains have been carved by erosion. This is a rather prevalent and persistent idea today, even in some high geological quarters.

Whatever the history of the height and relief of North Wales during Upper Palaeozoic and Mesozoic times may have been, geologists are agreed that it is likely that by early Tertiary times, at the latest, that region had become worn down to a low-lying, more or less level, surface. This surface may have been beneath the sea in late Cretaceous times (but there are no deposits of Cretaceous Age) or a plain not far above sea-level. Geologists are agreed that this surface was later raised by stresses in the earth's crust probably as a distant effect of the Alpine movements in the Miocene period—effects seen in sharp folding in south-east England and in the gentle tilt to the south-east of the Mesozoic rocks of the Midlands. The supposed dome-shaped mass whose surface is envisaged as coinciding with the present hill-top surface might thus (it has been suggested) have been formed by this uplift. But there are what appear to be fatal objections to this idea.

It seems almost impossible that deep valleys should be cut into an uplifted land-surface leaving the other parts of that surface unaffected, that is, not appreciably lowered. Even were that possible, it would be an extremely rare chance that we should anywhere 'catch' the process of erosion when it had gone just so far as to have produced peaks and ridges between the valleys, the summits still remaining intact at the original surface of the uplifted land. Can it be supposed that those summits would not have been, and are not continuing to be, worn down by erosion? If it is granted (as surely it must be) that the present imaginary hill-top surface is an eroded surface, then any original uplifted surface, at a higher, perhaps a much higher, level, will have been completely lost.

The form of the present actual relief depends on : (1) the production of the curve of subaerial erosion : a principle which applies to the formation of river-valleys, intervening ridges and indeed, to all parts of the surface; (2) the pattern and location of the main valleys which might be due either to previous geological conditions (as in the case of superimposed drainage) or be largely a matter of chance; and (3) the principle of the differ-

E

ential erosion of harder and softer rocks, so that the harder rocks all the time tend to remain the higher.

It is, however, highly probable, if not virtually certain, that any uplifted original unmodified surface never really existed. Erosion, both subaerial and marine, would start its work as soon as the plain began to rise. It would never reach the height or assume the form that would have been produced by the earth-movement alone.

There is obviously a correspondence between the lower and middle Ordovician rocks, reinforced as they are with igneous intercalations, and the regions of the higher mountain on the one hand; and between the entirely sedimentary Cambrian and upper Ordovician (and succeeding Silurian) and a lower hill-top surface on the other. But within the mountain area of Snowdonia it can hardly be said that there is a regular correspondence between the outcrops of what one would take to be the more resistant rocks and the height of the ground they occupy. It seems that the chance factor (no 2 above) might be responsible for this condition.

Sources and historical notes
Sedgwick began his famous campaign of investigation into the geological structure of North Wales in 1831 and all his most important discoveries were made in the early 1830s. Apart from notices of verbal discourses in the minutes of meetings of the Cambridge Philosophical Society and the British Association, very few facts were published until inadequate editorial reports and rather rambling papers by Sedgwick himself appeared in the *Proceedings of the Geological Society* (1838, 1843) and the *Quarterly Journal* (1845, 1847, 1852). Sedgwick was extremely careless about publication and it is only by a most fortunate chance that three very rough, but revealing, sketch sections, made in 1832, were preserved and published. These were in a letter to Murchison scribbled to 'fill up this sheet with one or two sections for your amusement' (Clark and Hughes, 1890, p394). The map showing the main structural lines, probably made at much the same time, was not published till 1845 (reproduced by Bassett, 1969).

Mapping by the Geological Survey was begun in 1846 and between 1850 and 1854 the maps were published on the scale of 1in to the mile and sections on the scale of 6in to the mile along lines surveyed in special detail.

> Ramsay and his colleagues delineated the outcrops of the pyroclastic, extrusive and intrusive rocks with remarkable accuracy. They produced maps of superb quality which, together with the accompanying Memoir (1866, 1881), remain the only comprehensive publications on the region as a whole. The irregularities [of structure] noted by Ramsay became much more obvious as a new generation of geologists remapped parts of the region during the years between the two world wars. New lines were added and the revision produced a wealth of stratigraphical, petrological and structural data, all of which revealed the complexity of the geology of the area. (Bassett, 1969)

The chief works of this 'new generation' were those of Howel Williams, 1922, 1927 (on Snowdon, specially important), 1930 and (with Bulman) 1931; David Williams, 1930; and Davies, 1936. Meanwhile Harker's classic 'Sedgwick prize essay' on 'The Bala Volcanic series of Caernarvonshire' had appeared (1889) and Gertrude Elles's study of the Conway area (1909). During the last twenty years there has been a renewed and sustained burst of activity, with the discovery of new structures and new kinds of igneous rock, particularly the volcanic ignimbrites. The following works are in our bibliography: Shackleton, 1953, 1959; Rast, 1960, 1961, 1962, 1969; Rast, Beavon, and Fitch, 1958, 1959, 1961; Beavon, 1963; Fitch, 1967, 1971; Bromley, 1969; Roberts, 1967, 1969; Brenchley, 1969.

The authoritative technical summary of the geology is that in George's revision of the Regional Geology handbook (1961), though this does not include the latest findings on the nature of the volcanic rocks. North's part of the Snowdonia National Park volume (1949) is a small masterpiece of geological summary, and the pamphlet on the 'Classic British area: Snowdonia' (D. Williams and J. G. Ramsay, 1968) is one of the best of the Geologists' Association's excursion guides.

For the description of the glacial phenomena there are two outstanding works. The first is Andrew Ramsay's *Old Glaciers of North Wales* (1860) which deals also with Switzerland. This book is probably the shortest of all the 'classics' of British geology. The other is the paper in the Geological Society's *Journal* (1909) by the famous American geomorphologist, W. M. Davis, on glacial erosion in Snowdonia.

CHAPTER 7

The Harlech Dome

The country is wild and mountainous and of high relief, the highest ground being formed largely of the hard and massive grits which constitute so much of the lower half of the Cambrian succession. The chief heights above 2,000ft are Y Llethr (2,475), Diffwys (2,462), Rhinog Fawr (2,362), Rhinog Fach (2,333), and Y Garn (2,063). The characteristic scenery of the grit country (especially well shown by the Rhinog Grits), whenever the dips are low and undulating, is a succession of scarps and terraces. The coastal region is, for the most part, a low platform of varying width, accreted to the land since glacial time, with the old marine cliffs at its inland edge. (Matley and Wilson, slightly adapted)

Succession

Structure

The Merioneth Dome, of which the central part is called the Harlech Dome, is the largest individual geological structure in North Wales (fig 21). It is cut into by the sea on the west so that on that side about one-third of it is hidden. It is clearly defined by the ring of Ordovician volcanic rocks round its outer parts. The central part of the dome is occupied by Cambrian rocks and there are presumably Pre-Cambrian rocks hidden underneath in the core. Here in this central part the dips are more undulating and irregular than they are on the flanks, there being several comparatively minor folds with their axes aligned roughly north and south; of these an anticline on the east brings

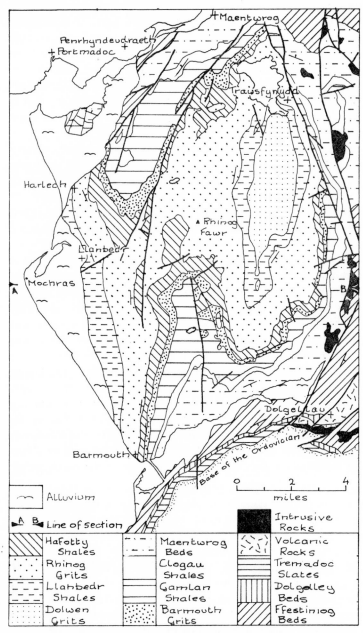

Fig 21 Geological map of the Harlech Dome (*principally after Matley and Wilson, 1946*)

up the lowest rocks seen in the dome in an elliptical outcrop, and on the west is a long syncline in two parts, in echelon. It is to be supposed that there is a concealed anticlinal structure farther west and there is in fact the northerly tip of such an anticline in the rocks round Tremadoc. At one time it was thought that Arvonian rocks (lowest Cambrian or Pre-Cambrian) were to be seen *in situ* on Sarn Badrig, well out to sea, but it has been found that all the 'causeway' is formed of loose pebbles and boulders.

The exposed strata are broken by a number of faults, mostly slightly oblique to the fold axes and the stratal strike. It is provisionally assumed that all the faulting, while seen to have occurred after the folding (because the fold-structures are cut through), is all a part, together with the folding, of the deformation that occurred at the end of Silurian times; but of this we cannot be certain.

Very important results have recently been obtained from a borehole drilled from a point situated among the sandhills at Mochras, 2 miles west of Llanbedr, where the land, here covered with superficial deposits, projects farthest into the sea. This reached a depth of over 6,000ft (nearly 2,000 metres) and, surprisingly, penetrated a succession from glacial deposits downward through strata, probably Tertiary, into undoubted Liassic strata with their characteristic fossils and ending in the Upper Triassic. This seemed to indicate a great fault of Tertiary age, with a large vertical component of throw to the west, running north and south within a mile or so to the east of the boring (fig 22). In that case the missing third of our structure of Cambrian rocks has been cut off from the visible two-thirds and let down for thousands of feet. But what has become of the north end of

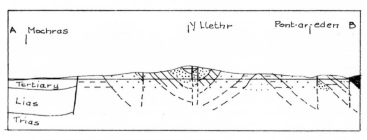

Fig 22   East-west cross-section through the Harlech Dome

the fault? The Cambrian and Ordovician rocks carry on west-wards through the Lleyn peninsula without any sign of it. That the basin of Mesozoic and Tertiary sedimentation is bounded on its east side by a fault, and not by a slope of Lower Palaeozoic rocks against which these much newer rocks were banked, remains conjectural.

It must be clearly understood that the term 'dome' refers to the structural arrangement of the rock-groups and not to the incidental fact that the hill-top surface of this central part might be said to be in the form of a greatly flattened dome. The discussion of the hill-top surface of central Caernarvonshire could be equally well applied to central Merioneth.

Dolwen Grits
This is the lowest of the formations exposed in the region and occupies an elliptical outcrop in the central part of the eastern anticline. The base is nowhere seen; as George puts it, 'the arching of the Harlech Dome not being sufficiently acute and erosion not having proceeded sufficiently deeply to expose the floor'. Notwithstanding the general grit lithology, the rocks form relatively low ground, occupying 'a dreary and desolate moorland of boulder-clay traversed by sluggish streams that flow through bog and peat' (Matley). The rocks are thus poorly exposed. Dolwen is in the heart of the outcrop.

Llanbedr Slates
Imperfectly cleaved blue and purple slates with frequent inter-calations of arenaceous beds. Between Harlech and Llanbedr the group is exposed along the pre-glacial sea-cliffs but farther south this western outcrop is buried beneath drift.

Rhinog Grits
Coarse, massively-bedded, and strongly jointed. Conglomeratic beds contain pebbles, many of which match rocks in the (Pre-Cambrian) Mona Complex. It is the dominant member of the Harlech series, forming most of the high ground in the central part of the region. The toughness, combined with an even and moderate dip, results in blocky upstanding mountains, quite different from those carved from the Ordovician volcanic rocks.

Hafotty Shales

Shales and flags with some grits. About 30ft above the base is a manganese ore-bed about a foot thick. It is a hard siliceous laminated band, evidently laid down as a sediment, perhaps in a shallow lagoon. Its distinctive character and its wide persistence at the same stratigraphical level throughout the area has been a great help in providing a datum plane in geological mapping. The whole group is often called the 'Manganese Shales'. It is well seen at Barmouth (fig 23), the old Hafotty mines being on the hillside a mile or so north of the town.

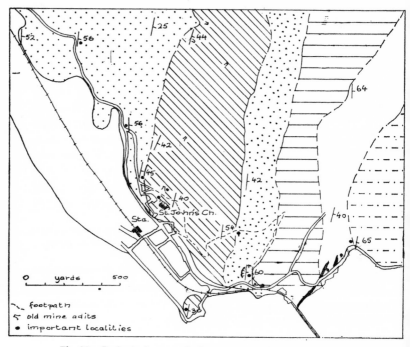

Fig 23   Geological map of the area round Barmouth town

Barmouth Grits

The lithology and structure are similar to those of the Rhinog Grits and much the some type of scenery results. 'These grits form the long ridge of the Llawllech, extending inland from Barmouth and culminating in Diffwys. They then swing southwards across the anticline of the Cwm Mynach valley and form the fine scarp of the western slopes of Y Garn' (Cox and Wells). At Barmouth the grits produce a high, steep, rough and craggy outcrop; most of the town was built of stone from the great quarry there. By the road side just east of the quarry is seen the transition from the grits to the succeeding Gamlan Shales (fig 24).

Fig 24 The top of the Barmouth Grits, followed by the lowest Gamlan Shales, exposed in a roadside cutting at the east end of Barmouth

Gamlan Shales
With beds of grit. An interesting feature is the presence of abundant so-called 'worm tubes', the origin of which is obscure.

These six groups, from the Dolwen Grits to the Gamlan Shales, constitute the Harlech series, which forms the main upstanding mass of the central part of the structural dome. As all the members are unfossiliferous it is impossible to place them directly on the general stratigraphical scale. As the next group, the Clogau Shales, following on conformably, contains fossils of the upper diversion of the Middle Cambrian, the Harlech series must span the lower division of the Middle Cambrian in its upper part down to an unknown depth in the Lower Cambrian. It is thus uncertain where the division should be drawn here be-

tween Lower and Middle Cambrian. When it is wished to fit the
succession somehow into the general classification a provisional
line is usually drawn at the top of the Hafotty (Manganese)
Shales.

Clogau Shales

This group forms a narrow belt of relatively low and fertile
ground round the outcrop of the Harlech series. The rocks contain the earliest definite fossils so far found in the Merioneth
Dome, including the well-known trilobites *Paradoxides hicksi, P.
davidis, Eodiscus punctatus,* and various species of *Agnostus;*
there are also horny brachiopods. This formation is the equivalent of the Menevian formation of South Wales.

Lingula Flags

Three groups constitute this series: the Maentwrog, the Ffestiniog, and the Dolgelley. The rim of our part of the Dome is
formed of the lowest of these, the Maentwrog, followed outwards by the lower part of the Ffestiniog. The lithology of both
is, as the name implies, flaggy; but flags are infrequent in the
upper half of the Maentwrog group, the lower part of which
has been separately distinguished as the Vigra Flags. The individual flags are generally a few inches thick and produce a
'ribbon-banding' appearance when exposed in section on a cliff-
face. They have been called 'ringers', from the sound made when
hit with a hammer. The Maentwrog beds are well-exposed, for
instance in the road cuttings and cliff sections east of Barmouth,
where they show very conspicuously the characteristic 'rusty'
weathering, and along the route of the Panorama Walk above.
Fossils in this group include the trilobite *Olenus,* which determines the Upper Cambrian age of the rocks, and the long-ranging
little *Agnostus.*

Conditions of sedimentation

The lithological succession of the stratal groups in our area reveals a time-succession of alternate deposition of fine-grained and
coarse-grained sediments and this in turn points to a corresponding oscillation in the conditions of sedimentation. These conditions include (1) depth and quietness of water; (2) the nature of
the rocks being eroded on the neighbouring land; and (3) the

kind and power of transporting currents. Thus although we can examine the lithology, internal structure, petrology and microscopic petrography of the rocks in great detail, it is by no means easy to assess the exact conditions under which they were formed. So many factors are involved, and the same result may be produced in more than one way. Constituent mineral particles from the 'parent' rocks which are supplying the sediment are so thoroughly mixed and reassembled that they can tell practically nothing of their origin. Sizeable pebbles in a conglomerate may be revealing; but even here if, as we have mentioned in the case of the Rhinog Grits, pebbles can be matched with rock-types of a formation exposed in a particular place today, we can only say that that formation must have been exposed somewhere at that time.

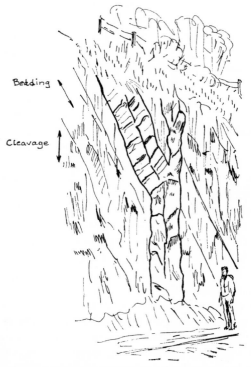

Fig 25   A roadside cutting with a dyke intruded into the Maentwrog beds, at Glan-dwr, two miles east of Barmouth on the Dolgelley road

Igneous rocks and metaliferous veins
There are very many small igneous intrusions (fig 25) chiefly
sills, among the rocks of the district. They include porphyritic
and doleritic types. Associated with these are quartz-veins containing ores; sulphides of various metals, together with free gold.

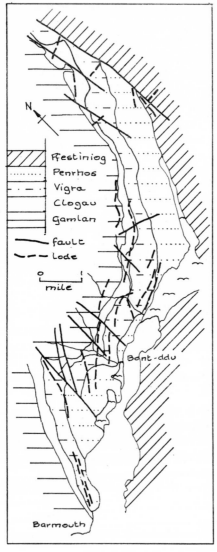

Fig 26   The gold-bearing
lodes   around   the   south-
eastern side of the Harlech
Dome (*after Andrew, 1910*)

The chief occurrences of these veins are in the Clogau Shales (fig 26). The intrusions and veins were doubtless formed in Ordovician times.

Sources and historical notes

For remarks on Sedgwick's work and publications on North Wales see the Snowdonia notes. His sections show 'the great Merioneth anticlinal', with its axis correctly placed east of the Rhinogs.

Mapping by the Geological Survey was begun in 1846 and the 1in maps were published between 1850 and 1854. Two groups were separated: the present Harlech series as 'Cambrian Sandstone, slate exceptional', and the present Clogau-Ffestiniog sequence as 'Lower Silurian, Lingula Flags etc.' The first edition of the large Memoir was published in 1866 with a map of the whole of Wales on the scale of 10 miles to 1in. All the essentials of the 1in maps are shown on this reduced scale. The map in the second edition (1881) is unchanged but in the text the Clogau beds are separately recognised as 'Menevian' and separated from the Lingula Flags.

Sedgwick had named his rocks 'Cambrian' in 1835 and had used the names 'Lingula Flags' and 'Ffestiniog group' in 1847 and 'Harlech Grits' in 1852. In 1867 Belt divided the Lingula Flags into these three series Maentwrog, Ffestiniog (redefined), Dolgelley.

In the 1900s the region was surveyed by Lapworth and Wilson but their work was not published until it was incorporated in the important paper by Matley and Wilson in 1946. Meanwhile Andrew's paper on the south-east part appeared in 1910 and Lapworth and Wilson's groups from the Dolwen Grits to the Clogau Shales were published.

The petrology of the Harlech series, particularly the mineralogy and petrology of the manganese ore, has been studied in detail by Woodland (1938, 1939, and in Matley and Wilson, 1946). Graphic and informative accounts of field-days spent in the area during the Geologists' Association's excursions to Dolgelley in 1927 and 1944 have been given by Cox and Wells (1927) and Cox and Lewis (1945). The structure was reviewed by Shackleton in 1953 and the history of its elucidation has recently been studied by Bassett (1969). Further historical details will be found in Matley and Wilson's paper and in the Regional Geology handbook (1961). Reference to the deposits of manganese ore are to be found in the books by Thomas (1961) and North (1962). These two books also give short accounts of the history of the 'Dolgelley gold belt', more particularly described by Andrew (1910).

The Llanbedr borehole is fully documented in the report edited by Woodland (1971).

CHAPTER 8

Criccieth to Portmadoc

There are many attractive geological and scenic features in this popular district.

> This area, forming the south-eastern corner of the county of Caernarvon, is a rectangular block of 20 square miles, and includes the townships of Portmadoc and Tremadoc (now united as the Urban District of Yynscynhaiarn) and the flourishing health-resorts of Borth-y-gest and Criccieth. For its scenery the district has long been famous, and there are few British districts which can show so great a variety of tide-flat, salt-marsh, sea-cliff, sand-dune, park, coppice, meadow, cornland, bog, moor, lake, and mountain, even over an area of many times its size. (Fearnsides)

The 'solid' geology of the area shows a triangular outcrop of Upper Cambrian rocks, with its apex in the north and its base the ragged coastline between Criccieth and Portmadoc, surrounded on the north-west and north-east by the outcrop of the lowest Ordovician rocks. This structure is partly concealed under glacial drift in the north and west of the area and under alluvium north and north-west of Portmadoc.

Succession

Ordovician	Arenig	Garth Grit
Cambrian	Upper (Tremadoc)	Garth Hill beds Penmorfa beds Portmadoc Flags Moel-y-gest beds Dictyonema band Tynllan beds
	Upper (Lingula Flags)	Dolgelley beds Ffestiniog beds Maentwrog beds

Structure

> The most outstanding characteristic of the geological map is the ring-like arrangement of the Lingula Flags and Tremadoc rocks

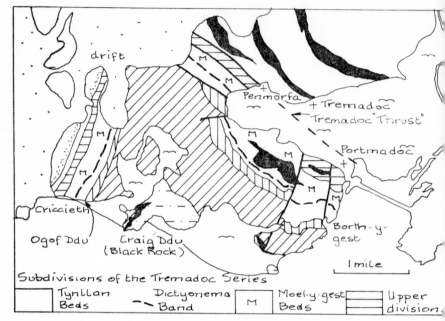

Fig 27   Geological map of the Portmadoc region. Symbols as for fig 21

about a centre which lies among the sandhills half a mile east of Craig Ddu and midway between Borth-y-gest and Criccieth (fig 27). From this centre, an anticline, with its axis pitching at about 1 in 6, ranges N 5°E through the marshes of Llyn Ystumllyn, and onwards until it is lost beneath the drift at Gwern-ddwyryd, half a mile beyond the village of Pentrefelin. From this axis the rocks dip away eastward at about 10° or 20°. To the westward the dip is steeper. (Fearnsides)

The Tremadoc series of rocks is followed apparently conformably by coarse sandy and conglomeratic beds long known in this area as the Garth Grit, named from the hill, Y Garth, across the Afon Glaslyn to the east. Beds of this lithological character are held to indicate very shallow water conditions of deposition and they are usually impersistent laterally owing to the restricted area of such conditions. When they are extensive they will indicate a transgression of the sea over the land, spreading these conditions as the sea advances; conglomerates immediately overlie a surface of unconformity. Such a transgression is usually more or less gradual, with overlap of the higher members of the series of beds over the lower. The conglomerates, being laid down all the time as the sea advances, will be diachronous, that is, they will not represent one period of time. But the Garth Grit is exceptional and is everywhere in the same stratigraphical position in relation to the overlying beds over the whole of its widespread occurrence in North Wales. Nearly everywhere, except in this Tremadoc country and the Deudraeth country immediately to the east, the Garth Grit is unconformable to the rocks below, this unconformity being most marked in the western parts of Lleyn where, in the St Tudwal's peninsula, it rests on various members of the Cambrian system and farther west still on the Pre-Cambrian (see our section on the Lleyn region). This widespread, and in parts profound, unconformity indicates a geologically sudden marine transgression over a land that had been locally upheaved with tilting and folding of the previously deposited strata and great erosion of them. Deposition in our present area must have been practically continuous, as the Garth Grit is not only structurally conformable to the underlying strata but these strata are known to be, by their fossils, at the top of the Cambrian system. There can therefore be little, if anything, of a non-sequence, representing a period of no deposition. It is evident, however, that there was a sudden change from the quiet conditions of deposition of latest Tremadoc times, because the conglomerates of the Garth Grit abruptly follow the mudstones of the uppermost Tremadoc strata.

One curious feature nearly everywhere about the basal part of the Garth Grit is the occurrence in it of *Bolopora undosa*, a somewhat problematical object, but supposed to be 'a rock-building bryozoan with phosphatised skeleton' (Lewis).

As the Garth Grit not only widely defines the base of a new series in North Wales but is everywhere at about the same stratigraphical horizon, its base is obviously a most convenient level at which to draw a line in the classification of the strata. On the general world-wide classification, the equivalents of our Tremadoc series ('Tremadocian' is a term widely used beyond Wales) are usually placed in the Ordovician, rather than in the Cambrian, system, chiefly because the fossil fauna is more allied to Ordovician rather than Cambrian faunas: and there is a tendency to adopt this grouping for the British rocks. But in North

F

Wales the Tremadoc series is so firmly allied stratigraphically to the rocks below that it would be unfortunate if we had to put it here in the Ordovician rather than leave it in the Cambrian, in which it was placed when Lapworth redefined that system in 1889.

A very prominent structural feature of this region and in the Deudraeth region to the east is the occurrence of thrust faulting at about the horizon of the Cambrian-Ordovician boundary. In places this has caused a confusion of the stratigraphy, repeating some beds and cutting out others. This is not so marked in this Tremadoc area as it is in the Deudraeth country but the series of parallel shatterings which run north-west to south-east about the village of Penmorfa cuts out the Garth Grit altogether. On the western side of the anticline, strata both in the uppermost Cambrian and the lowermost Ordovician are broken into lenticles some hundreds of feet in extent along the strike.

All the secondary structural features were imposed on the strata during the period of deformation at the end of Silurian times. In addition to the folding and faulting all the finer-grained rocks were converted to slates.

Igneous rocks
Very conspicuous are the igneous rocks of the area; conspicuous topographically because, being relatively resistant to erosion, they form hills and headlands, and conspicuous geologically because of their distinctive petrographical character. Being emplaced among the strata the question of their geological age naturally arises. In this case, as in the case of the intrusions of Snowdonia, were they directly connected with the Ordovician volcanicity or were they intruded at the end of Silurian times (or even later)? The north-east corner of our area forms a part of the Snowdonian area and there are many volcanic rocks of the Snowdon Volcanic series there. The smaller intrusions certainly seem to have been affected by the same pressures that produced slaty cleavage in the neighbouring rocks, and it is probable that all the intrusions are connected with the Ordovician volcanicity, as seems to be the case throughout Snowdonia.

There are small sills of dolerite intruded along a stratigraphical horizon (which has been taken here as that separating the Maentwrog and Ffestiniog beds). They take part in the folding and this in itself strongly suggests that they were intruded before the folding occurred; but sills could be intruded along horizons already not too strongly folded. The most prominent of these sills is that which forms the ridge and little projecting Craig Ddu, the Black Rock, one mile east of Criccieth.

There are larger sills, perhaps of a somewhat laccolitic form, one of which forms the outstanding handsome hill of Moel-y-Gest (fig 28). These are coarser in texture, 'gabbroid dolerites', as one would expect from their larger size and therefore slower cooling.

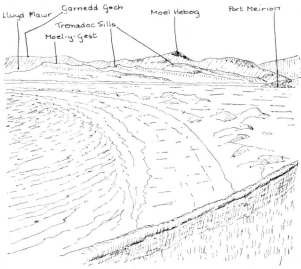

Fig 28   View of the southern Snowdonian and Portmadoc region from near Harlech

Cambrian rocks

The Cambrian formations provide many interesting features of lithology and structure. To describe these details here would make this account too long; but it may be said that to go carefully over the ground with Fearnsides's paper (or copious notes from it) in hand is a very rewarding experience in field geology.

The following is from Fearnsides and Davies's paper on the 'Deudraeth' area, which adjoins the Portmadoc area on the east:

Garth Hill beds (Upper Tremadoc Slates). In these beds the characteristic *Angelina sedgwicki* is abundant in certain layers, occasion-

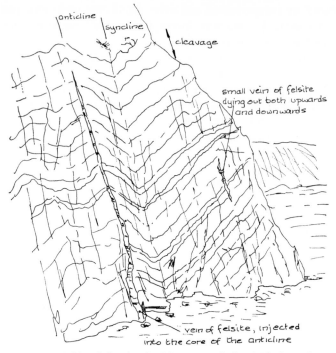

Fig 29   Felsite dykes in the Maentwrog beds of Black Rock

ally associated with other fossils. Homfray's famous collecting ground, the slabs along the Glaslyn river frontage north of Y Garth, has been cleared and almost devastated by collectors. Occasional whole trilobites may still be obtained from the dip-slope farther east, or unearthed by excavation of suitable blocks about Plas-newydd and Bron Gelynen on the south side of the dolerite intrusion.

A salutary caution is contained in this quotation. Though no doubt the rocks hold in depth an almost inexhaustible treasure of fossils, these only become visible and available to the collec-tor over the extremely limited areas where the rocks are ex-posed. Moreover, the best places for collecting are those where the fossils are not only plentifully present in the rocks but where these rocks have been just so far weathered as to be readily split with the hammer to reveal and to yield the fossils, still intact but separable from the matrix. Such exposures are thus rare and the better-known ones are very liable to be 'cleared and devastated' by inexperienced and over-enthusiastic collectors, particularly when parties may follow each other year after year, and perhaps week after week.

The fossils from the Tremadoc Slates series have usually been distorted by the pressure which produced the cleavage, although this may still not have been enough to destroy skeletal details. One thinks particularly of the many fine museum specimens of *Angelina sedgwicki* from the Garth Hill locality, lengthened, shortened, or obliquely distorted.

Sources and historical notes
Information which would fall into this section has already been given or hinted at in various parts of our account, which is based almost entirely on Fearnsides's paper in the *Quarterly Journal* for 1910. He has a section on the 'Previous literature'. His account of the Geologists' Association excursion in 1912 is also full of interest. Apart from the earlier work of Sedgwick, Davis, and Sharpe, by far the most important research before Fearnsides's time was that carried out by Salter as part of the Geological Survey team under Ramsay. His work is recorded in the two successive editions of the Memoir (1866, 1881).

CHAPTER 9

Cader Idris and Neighbouring Areas

The mountain-range of Cader Idris (the chair or seat of Idris, a mythical Welsh giant) is formed by a great escarpment of Ordovician volcanic rocks which looks northwards across the Mawddach estuary towards the extensive area of Lower Cambrian rocks comprised in the Harlech Dome. The range has a general east-north-east to west-south-west trend, but the central portion runs almost due east and west. Along the range are several summits, all exceeding

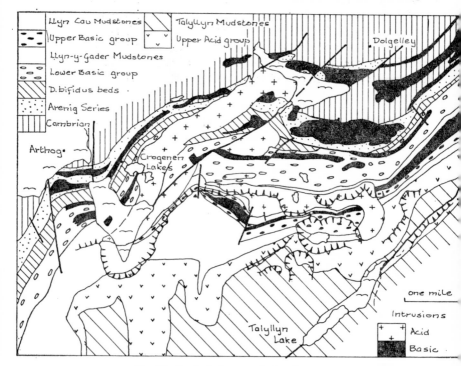

Fig 30 Geological map of the Cader Idris region
(after Cox and Wells, 1927)

2,000ft in altitude. The range is bounded on the south by the Talyllyn valley, and on the north by the valley running from Dolgelley past Llyn Gwernan. Both these valleys trend nearly northeast to south-west, and follow the lines of repeating faults. North of the Llyn Gwernan valley, a smaller hill-range, or rather a series of ranges, intersected by the Gwynant valley, intervenes between Cader Idris and the Mawddach estuary. (Cox)

Succession

Ordovician	Lower Bala (Caradoc) (? with Llandeilo)	Tal-y-llyn Mudstones Upper Acid group Llyn Cau Mudstones Upper Basic group Llyn-y-Gader Mudstones & Ashes Oolitic Iron-ore band
	Llanvirn	Lower Basic group Cefn Hir Ashes
	Arenig	Bifidus beds Lower Acid group Basement beds
Cambrian	Tremadoc	

Structure

On the whole the structure is fairly simple, especially when we compare it with the structure of some other areas in Wales occupied by Lower Palaeozoic rocks. The region is situated along the southern part of the Merioneth or Harlech Dome, but whereas in the central part of this structure the dips are wayward, here they are quite decided and regular at about 40° to the south or south-south-east (fig 31).

The succession given above lists only the formations that

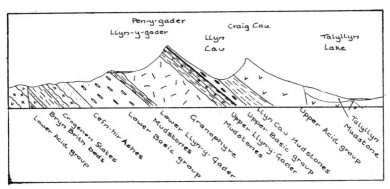

Fig 31 Cross-section through Cader Idris (*after Cox, 1925*)

occur regularly stratified one above the other and representing
a continuous passage of time. In this succession as named are two
main kinds of rock: (1) the ordinary sedimentary formations
called 'beds', 'mudstones'; and (2) the volcanic rocks, 'ashes', and
'acid' and 'basic' groups. In addition there are those igneous
intrusions which being of a sill-like disposition (though of
limited lateral extent) take part, more or less locally at various
levels, in the actual build of the rock-pile. They are, in fact,
'intruders' into the proper sequence and have to be considered
separately both as regards their form, manner of emplacement,
and age. The even structure is thus in the first place interfered
with by the occurrence of these intrusions at several levels and
in various parts.

Quite a different kind of complication is introduced by minor
tectonic features. There are small folds with axes aligned north
and south and small dip-faults. There are small strike-faults
mostly with downthrow to the south 'with the dip', thus pre-
venting ('cutting out') the outcrop of some beds. But the most
important fault is the large strike-fault which enters our region
from the north-east, passes south of Dolgelley and on past Llyn
Gwernan, beyond which it is responsible for the long straight
valley followed by the old Towyn Road. This throws down to
the north (there may be some lateral, or 'tear', movement as
well) with a consequent repetition of outcrops.

Thus for purely structural reasons the geological map is not
so simple in detail. In any case a geological map in mountainous country is not likely to have a simple face to it because
outcrops depend on surface relief. Unless this relief is itself entirely determined by the outcrops or unless the dips are everywhere vertical—either state of affairs being altogether exceptional—the course of the lines on the geological map will be
affected by the relief.

There is a conformable succession of stratigraphical formations from those with a Cambrian (Tremadocian) fossil fauna
into those with an early Ordovician fauna, but there is no difficulty in drawing a line between the Cambrian and Ordovician
in this district as we have conglomerates and grits following
the Tremadocian just as is the case in the Portmadoc district, and
the base of the Ordovician (Arenig) is taken at their base. We
evidently have the equivalent formation to the Garth Grit of

that northern area, and again the base is characterised by the peculiar *Bolopora undosa*. As in the Portmadoc area the sudden change in lithology, combined with the knowledge of the unconformity at the base of this formation in the extreme north-western parts of Wales, may indicate something of a non-sequence.

Some details

We are here concerned with the geology of the Ordovician rocks from the foothills on the north side of Cader Idris, up and over that mountain, and down to the Tal-y-llyn valley on the south. This takes us through an upward succession of rock-formations; but the most convenient itinerary goes the opposite way, starting near Doy-y-Cau in the Tal-y-llyn valley and ending at Llyn Gwernan.

The sedimentary rocks and igneous volcanic rocks occur in an orderly sequence, as already tabulated, and the structural occurrence of the igneous intrusions (which are later than the adjacent rocks) has been stated in a general way.

It remains to consider some of the particular facts and the inferences to be drawn from them as regards modes of formation, the geography of the times, and when those times were on the general geological time-scale.

The sedimentary rocks are in general mudstones, more or less cleaved (the Bifidus beds are commercially workable slates), with some volcanic ashes. However, the Basement beds are coarser (with the conglomerate at the base) except near the top where at one locality shales have yielded fragmental graptolites characteristic of the zone of *Didymograptus hirundo*, the upper of the two Arenig zones. The Bifudus beds are named from the occurrence of *Didymograptus bifidus*, with other species of that zone. Thus in this lower part of the succession we have two local stratigraphical horizons fixed on the general scale. Graptolites in the Llyn-y-Gader Mudstones and the Llyn Cau Mudstones are poorly preserved but indicate the zone of *Nemagraptus gracilis*. As in North Wales generally it is not certain whether there are any sedimentary rocks which were laid down during the time covered by the *Glyptograptus teretiusculus* zone, that is, during 'Llandeilo time' as nowadays restricted. Incidentally, this graptolite is an unfortunate one to be chosen as a zonal index species. It is not too easy to identify in poorly preserved specimens; and it is repeatedly mentioned in the accounts of our present region as occurring together with the graptolites of the *Nemagraptus gracilis* zone.

At the base of the Llyn-y-Gader Mudstones, over a very wide area, is a band of oolitic iron ore. It is considered that this has not resulted from the alteration of oolitic limestones (as is often the case) but is probably a primary deposit, the result of bacterial and algal action.

The Tal-y-llyn Mudstones are practically unfossiliferous but they are succeeded by beds containing graptolites of the *Dicranograptus clingani* zone. Thus it seems that they represent the zones of *Climacograptus peltifer* and *Climacograptus wilsoni*, which intervene between the *gracilis* zone and the *clingani* zone. The Appendix lists the graptolite zones of the Ordovician.

The igneous rocks emitted at the surface, that is the 'volcanic' rocks as usually understood by the term, are of two contrasted types (composition and manner of emission going together, as is usually the case): acid rocks of restricted areal extent, and more widespread basic lavas. These latter are in many places 'pillow-lavas' (cf fig 59), a name which indicates their appearance, and as regards composition they are the particular variety, spilites, as most pillow-lavas are. The acid rocks have been called 'rhyolites' (lavas) and 'ashes' or 'tuffs' (pyroclastics), but it now appears likely that most of both these types are 'ignimbrites', the special kind of essentially pyroclastic rock. For this question see the discussion in our Snowdonia section.

During much of Ordovican time we may imagine our region to have been an extensive more or less shallow sea studded with volcanic islands which periodically spread their eruptive materials over the normal sediment.

Ingeous intrusions

These have been authoritatively described by Cox and Wells, and in the following paragraphs we closely follow their account:

It is highly probable that each of the volcanic phases was accompanied by the injection of some minor intrusions. These intrusions fall into two main groups: acid (granophyres) and basic (dolerites).

The granophyres comprise two short thick sills or laccolites and several smaller bodies. Of the larger sills the one occurs in the foot-hills of the Cader range and the other forms the most striking feature in the main escarpment itself (fig 32); the former is known as the Crogenen sill and the latter as the Llyn-y-Gader laccolite or sill.

Fig 32 The scarp of Cader Idris seen from the Dinas Mawddwy road

The Crogenen sill, about 1,200ft thick, is traceable along the strike for approximately five miles. In that distance it transgresses from the Tremadoc Slates at its north-east end to the Llyn Cau Mudstones at its south-west end, that is, it is a 'transgressive sill'. Thus when injected it must have risen along an inclined plane rising towards the south west. Its outcrop is now repeated by strike-faulting, so that it appears on both sides of the Gwernan fault-valley. Unlike most of the igneous rocks in the district, the Crogenen granophyre forms chiefly low-lying ground, this being due to an intricate, small-scale jointing which has facilitated its degradation and removal by ice and other denuding agents. In this respect it is unlike the higher sill, to whose presence the escarpment of Cader Idris is largely due.

The Llyn-y-Gader laccolite is a thick concordant intrusion, 2,000ft in thickness, which maintains its level at one and the same horizon (in the Llyn-y-Gader Mudstones) for a distance of three miles, representing the greater part of its outcrop (figs 33, 34). At its western end it terminates abruptly in the same rocks, but towards its eastern extremity it suddenly transgresses onto higher horizons as far as the base of the highest (Upper Acid) volcanic series. As at this point (on Mynydd Moel) an anticlinal flexure crosses the escarpment; it is probable that the magma rose here, penetrating almost vertically until stopped by the practically impenetrable cover of the acid lavas, and then spread

Fig 33   The north-facing scarp of Cader Idris from Cyfrwy
(*after Cox, 1925*)

Fig 34   The north-facing scarp of Cader Idris, from Llyn-y-Gader
(*after Cox, 1925*)

G: granophyre; D: dolerite; M; mudstones; A: ashes; P: pillow lava

laterally along the nearest plane of easy passage.

In respect of the ratio of breadth to height, the Llyn-y-Gader
intrusion falls within the limits prescribed for laccolites; further,

it has a flat base, somewhat arched roof, which was obviously lifted by the intrusive magma. The only unknown quality is the plan of the complete intrusion: should this originally have been approximately circular, the Llyn-y-Gader loccolite would be a very good example of this class of intrusion.

A striking columnar jointing traverses the laccolite from top to bottom (fig 34).

Basic sills occur at many horizons. Some are so closely similar petrographically to the extrusive spilites among which they were injected that there is no room for doubt as to their consanguinity: they represent spilitic magma intruded beneath a thin cover of unconsolidated and water-charged sediment. In addition to the spilitic dolerites, which were nearly contemporaneous with the basic lavas, there are numerous, less localised intrusions of gabbroid dolerite of which the age is not so clear; but the invariable concentration of these dolerites in the volcanic tracts suggests a genetic relationship between the intrusive and extrusive rocks. That is, all the intrusions, acid and basic, are almost certainly of Ordovician age.

The largest individual doleritic intrusion in the neighbourhood is the Mynydd-y-Gader dolerite, described by Lake and Reynolds. Parts of this intrusion show a particularly regular columnar jointing (fig 33). Many of the now completely isolated dolerite outcrops must be regarded not as individual intrusions, but as portions of the same sheet severed by the accidents of faulting and denudation.

More recent studies, particularly of a petrochemical nature, of the dolerite near the summit of the mountain (the Pen-y-Gader dolerite) and the Llyn-y-Gader granophyre, and of their metamorphic effects on the adjacent rocks, have been made by R. G. Davies.

A sample of geology

The mountain of Cader Idris would provide a useful exercise in seeing how far one might obtain an insight into the science of geology by what one could observe and infer from this striking piece of country alone. That is, how far could the main principles of geology be explained from a much more limited region than the whole of North Wales? We shall not attempt to do that here, as it would involve a repetition of most of what we have already said in the first section of this book. We can how-ever emphasise the following steps in the argument. We start with the mountain just as we now see it and we make our ob-servations on it as it now stands. We next discuss processes of the formation of rocks in a general way and of these rocks in particular. Now we have to forget completely the geography as it exists today and keep our minds altogether on those entirely different geographies of past times which we have to envisage as a result of the reading of the geological history of this area (as part of a much larger area). It is only in the very last stages of the exercise that our mountain itself comes back into view as a result of the geomorphological evolution of recent geologi-cal times.

Plant distribution and rock outcrop

The flora of the mountains cannot fail to charm and interest the walker. This is certainly so in North Wales and there is here a special point in the connexion between the geology and the botany. We quote the following from William Condry's book on the *Snowdonia National Park*:

> Not only botanists but also some geologists take note of the luxur-iance of the vegetation on wet, lime-rich crags compared with its sparseness on drier, acid rocks. For instance, when H. Williams, in 1927, described the volcanic rock in Cwm Glas, he said it was 'un-usually calcareous and supports an abundant and typical flora. In-deed, in many places the accustomed eye can locate the outcrops of this series with reasonable accuracy by noting the contrast be-tween the patches of heather and bilberry that thrive on the underlying rhyolitic tuffs, and the rich green ferns and mosses that abound on the calcareous pumice-tuffs.' Similarly, the lime-rich pillow-lava band in the lower basic rocks of Cader Idris can be traced as clearly by botanists as it can by geologists, because along that band, but not above or below it, grow calcicole (lime-loving) plants such as green spleenwort, bladder fern, purple saxifrage, lesser meadow-rue, mountain sorrel, hairy rock-cress and numerous calcicole mosses.

The plant-distribution on Cader Idris was studied by Price Evans.

Neighbouring areas

We have taken Cader Idris as an example of the kind of Ordo-vician volcanic sequence found on the southern and eastern flanks of the Merioneth Dome. In other parts of this outcrop the sequence varies greatly in detail. For instance, Wells has shown that, on the mountain of Rhobell Fawr, very early Ordovician volcanic rocks rest unconformably on several successive members of the Upper Cambrian sequences and are themselves overlain by the basal Arenig (fig 35). Other areas are those of Arenig itself, described by Fearnsides, the Aran mountains, the survey

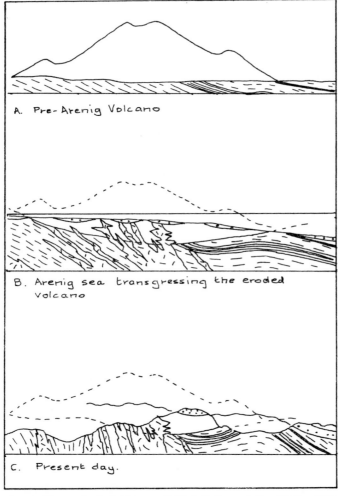

A. Pre-Arenig Volcano

B. Arenig sea transgressing the eroded Volcano

C. Present day.

Fig 35 The geological history of Rhobell Fawr (*after Wells, 1925*)

of which was begun by H. P. Lewis, and that between Fair-
bourne and Llwyngwril described by B. Jones.

South-eastwards of Cader Idris the Upper Acid volcanic group,
of Lower Bala or possibly Llandeilo age, is a sedimentary series
which is some 8,000ft thick between Tal-y-llyn and Corris. This
ranges from the Tal-y-llyn Mudstones or Ceiswyn beds of the
Lower Bala up to the top of the Upper Bala. The structure is
comparatively simple, with a general dip to the south-east, being
part of the south-eastern rim of the Merioneth Dome structure.
The lithology is a succession of mudstone and sandstone formations, some of the former being, rather locally, so greatly
cleaved as to form commercially quarriable slates. Throughout
the whole wide belt of these Bala rocks, from Towyn on the
coast to Bala itself 30 miles away to the north-east, there is a
gradual lateral lithological change from a preponderance of fine-
grained slaty mudstones with graptolites on the south-west to
coarser-grained rocks with shelly fossils towards the north-east.
In the Bala neighbourhood there are beds of limestone.

    Following to the south-east of the outcrops of the successive
members of the Bala series come those of the successive members of the Llandovery series of the Silurian. There is perfect
conformity between the two series but there is an abrupt change
in the lithology at the boundary. These lowest Llandovery beds,
belonging to the zone of *Glyptograptus persculptus*, are hard,
peculiarly mottled mudstones which makes them easily mapped,
and this is helped by their forming a little escarpment. Higher
zones follow until the Afon Dyfi is reached, and beyond this
river, near Machynlleth, we come into the northern end of the
dome structure to be mentioned in our section on Northern
Cardiganshire.

One of the longest traceable structural features in North Wales
is the great fault, or fault-belt, that runs fairly straight from
Towyn to Bala, usually called the 'Bala Fault'. Nearly all the
way erosion has carved out a trench owing to the relative weakness of the greatly disturbed and broken rocks along it. The
'fault' is probably a series of closely-spaced parallel faults, a
'shatter-belt'. The trench is most conspicuous at Tal-y-llyn (fig
36) and thence to the sea at Towyn.

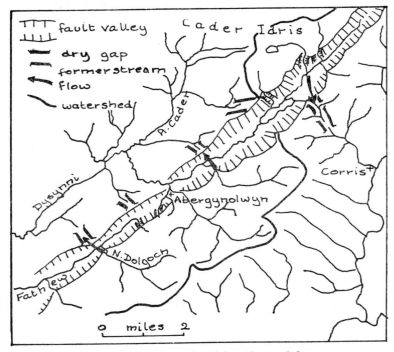

Fig 36 Present rivers in the Cader Idris region, and former courses
indicated by the dry gaps (*after Watson, 1962*)

For the most part the course of the fault lies just to the north
of the areas of Bala rocks whose stratigraphy has been studied
in detail. It is very difficult to assess its 'geometrical' effects on
the strata, because particular beds and particular structural
features, especially fold-axes, are difficult to recognise on each
side of the fault. It is probably in the main a 'tear', 'wrench', or
'transcurrent', fault (the terms are synonymous), with southwesterly movement on the north-west side relative to the south-
east side, a 'sinistral transcurrent' fault. But there may also be a
component of downthrow on the north-west side and, further, it
may be to some extent a 'thrust fault' with over-riding from the
south-east. If we imagine pressure from the south this would
tend to cause both thrusting and sliding in the directions named
if the rock-structure broke obliquely in a south-west to north-
east direction. The fault might then be said to come in the category of faults recently recognised as 'transpression' faults.

G

The age of the fault is also uncertain. It is probably a part of the structural deformation produced all over our area of north-west Wales at the end of Silurian times. We cannot tell whether further movement occurred along it after Carboniferous times; there are faults affecting the Carboniferous rocks in north-eastern Wales, but we do not know whether these are at all connected in time with the Bala Fault.

Sources and historical notes
The region was surveyed by the Geological Survey and the 1in map was first published in 1850. The account of the geology is contained in the large Memoir of 1866, with its second edition of 1881. The Regional Geology handbook (George, 1961) shows the original Geological Survey section from north to south and, for comparison, a section compiled from the work of the more recent workers which confirms the main features of the early one. 'Ramsay and his colleagues during their pioneer survey determined both the rock sequence and the geological structure with high accuracy.'

The era of modern research divides into two periods. In the 1920s detailed accounts were published in the *Quarterly Journal* of the Geological Society on the Arthog-Dolgelley strip of country (Cox and Wells, 1920) and on Cader Idris itself (Cox, 1925). Their findings were collected together in a most useful account, with itineraries, in the Geologists' Association *Proceedings* (1927). Some notes are also contained in the report of a second 'field meeting' in 1944 (Cox and Lewis, 1945).

In the 1950s and 1960s we have the researches, involving the latest petrographical and petrochemical methods, of R. G. Davies, with theoretical considerations and itineraries by him and by W. J. Phillips (Davies, 1956, 1959, 1967; Phillips, 1966).

The glacial features of the Dolgelley district have been described by Miller (1946) and the dramatic land-forms, so largely due to glaciation, of Cader Idris and the Tal-y-llyn valley, by Watson (1960, 1962; conveniently summarised in 1969).

The papers referred to in the paragraph on the several other areas of the volcanic sequence are: Wells (1925); Fearnsides (1905); Lewis (1936); B. Jones (1933).

Detailed accounts of the Ordovician and Silurian rocks to the south-east of the Cader Idris range are to be found in the following works, reading from south-west to north-east: Jehu (1926); Pugh (1923, 1928, 1929); Elles (1922); Bassett, Whittington and Williams (1966). There is a general account (excluding the Bala country) in Jones and Pugh (1935).

The questions concerning the Bala Fault have been considered particularly by Jehu (1926) and Basset (1969).

CHAPTER 10

Northern Cardiganshire

For the purpose of explaining geology in Wales it was decided to draw the boundary between north and south across the middle of Cardiganshire. Here, in the northern part of the county, we have the mountain of Plynlimon and its satellite hills, very striking river scenery, a magnificent stretch of rocky coast: all provide a wealth of geology, but a geology still with unsolved problems and thus of particular interest. Here, too, is Aberystwyth—the seaside resort, university town, and home of the National Library of Wales.

Succession

Silurian	Llandovery	⎰ Ystwyth stage (including Aberystwyth Grits) ⎱ Pont-erwyd stage
Ordovician	Upper Bala (Ashgill)	Plynlimon stage

Lithological formations roughly mappable: (1) Plynlimon stage; (2) Aberystwyth Grits; (3) a predominantly shaly group comprising the Pont-erwyd stage and the Ystwyth stage, exclusive of the Aberystwyth Grits.

Structure

In investigating the structure of a piece of country the method normally adopted is quite straightforward, though it may be difficult to put into practice. This method is to make a geological map, drawing on an ordinary topographical map the boundaries of such rock groups as are recognisable by their lithological characters, and at the same time observing the disposition of these rock-groups and recording their dips. In this way the geological succession is built up and the foldings and dislocations revealed.

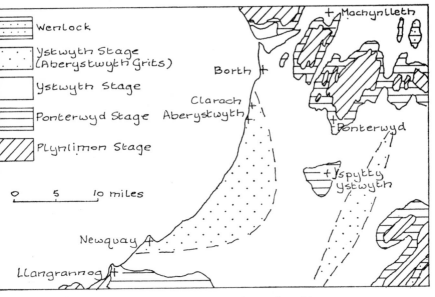

Fig 37 Geological map of north Cardiganshire
(*principally after O. T. Jones*)

This method, however, is applicable only to a very limited extent in Cardiganshire. In the first place it is difficult to distinguish and demarcate mappable groups. In the northern part of the county and in neighbouring areas there are three groups of strata that one can distinguish very roughly, but on the whole the lithology is monotonous, consisting of shales (with slaty cleavage) and 'grits'.

The first of these three groups is a predominantly gritty group over areas (a) between the rivers Llyfnant and Ceulan in the extreme north-west; (b) around Plynlimon; and (c) west of Llanidloes in Montgomeryshire. A second group is the Aberystwyth Grits formation, in the west, with its alternation of shaly mudstones and pale hard sandstones, predominantly fine-grained, the 'grit' beds; but although this lithology is characteristic where typically developed it is difficult to draw a boundary on the ground between the outcrop of this group and that of the third group. This third group is a predominantly shaly one (often with strongly-developed slaty cleavage) and its outcrop occupies the areas between the outcrops of the other two groups.

The second difficulty is the absence of regular dips. There are innumerable dips that can be recorded in the plentiful exposures, natural and artificial, along the coast and inland, but the strata are so highly folded that they have little value in revealing anything but local structures. In so far as there is any general appearance, by observing dips for some distances along the faces of the hills and noting scraps and dip-slopes in the landscape, there seems to be a general easterly dip, which would make the Aberystwyth Grits the lowest and Plynlimon rocks the highest of the three groups that, as we have noted, seem to be tentatively recognisable in a preliminary survey. This was the interpretation given in 1881 by Walter Keeping, one of the early professors at Aberystwyth. He made the rocks at Plynlimon into a syncline running north and south.

A particularly interesting feature of this episode is that Charles Lapworth, who had just established the stratigraphical value of graptolites in southern Scotland and to whom Keeping had sent some specimens from his several rock-groups, told Keeping that he had got his structure upside-down. But Keeping, while stating Lapworth's opinion, did not accept it.

It remained for O. T. Jones in 1909 and 1912 to confirm Lapworth's view, by the finding of many graptolites in the several rock-groups and careful mapping based principally on the contained fossils. This has resulted in the recognition of the Plynlimon Anticline, the Towy Anticline just beyond the southeastern border of the county, and the intervening Central Wales Syncline. Each of these main structures is composed of many minor folds, so that 'anticlinorium, and 'synclinorium' are the more correct terms. Also, they are more or less elongated boat-shaped folds, with the axes plunging towards the ends; indeed, the structure around Plynlimon approaches the nature of a dome.

Jones's findings established the stratigraphical succession that we have given in our table, using his names. It is his Pont-erwyd stage that is by far the most prolific in graptolites and which establishes the age of the beds most firmly and in most detail. The three 'stages' here enumerated do not quite correspond to the three roughly mappable lithological groups (see the note to the stratigraphical succession table). This Pont-erwyd stage, the lower part of the predominantly shaly group, occupies rather narrow bands surrounding the outcrops of the Plynlimon stage.

We must now mention an earlier, and very remarkable, episode in the history of our gradual understanding of the true structure of this part of Wales. (It may be taken as a generally understood principle that we cannot fully appreciate our present knowledge without knowing something of its history. This principle applies here with particular force.)

We have said that the detailed structure is very complicated and difficult to unravel. Curiously enough, the only attempt so far made to show this structure on a large scale is that which was made by A. C. Ramsay when he was in charge of the official Geological Survey of Wales in the middle of the last century. At that period the Geological Survey of Great Britain, wherever it was at work, made detailed traverses along certain lines, in addition to making smaller-scale (1in to the mile) geological maps, and the results were issued as sections on the scale of 6in to the mile. They were called (inappropriately) 'horizontal sections' to distinguish them from successions shown as columns, which were called 'vertical sections'. Two of Ramsay's sections, published in 1845, crossed Cardiganshire and although some of the minor folds were probably sketched in conjecturally, it was with extraordinary insight that he showed clearly the two anticlines and the intervening syncline.

The Cardiganshire rocks are affected by faults (figs 38, 39) which are of all sizes, from those a few yards long (in outcrop), and causing a dislocation of only a few inches, to those of some miles in length and causing a separation of some thousands of feet between points which were adjacent before the faulting.

Most of the larger faults are associated with the mineral lodes of the district and run roughly north-east to south-west. (The ores in the lodes are those of lead and zinc, together with associated ores of silver and copper.) There are, however, two faults, running more directly east and west, the Llyfnant Fault and the Ystwyth Fault, which are later than the other faults in their immediate neighbourhood, as shown by the fact that these other faults are dislocated by them.

The Llyfnant Fault was mapped by Jones and Pugh just before World War I and they estimated that where the movement had been greatest the strike-slip or 'tear' component was some five

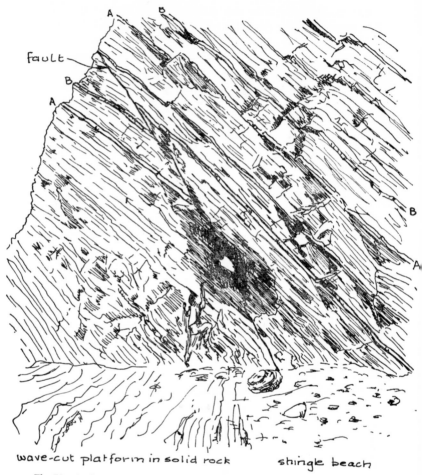

fault

wave-cut platform in solid rock   shingle beach

Fig 38 A thrust or reverse fault in the Aberystwyth Grits just north
of the promenade

times that of the dip-slip component.

The Ystwyth Fault has been traced for about 20 miles down
the length of the upper half of the Ystwyth valley, continuing
straight to the sea, along the valley of the Wyre, near Llanrhystyd. This evidently has little tear component of movement as
the south-south-west course of the axis of the Plylimon anticline
continues straight across it, with lower rocks now outcropping
round Yspytty Ystwyth on its southern side. The downthrow is

Fig 39 Small fault in the Aberystwyth Grits, north of Clarach

thus on its north side and the amount has been estimated at between 2,500 and 3,000ft. The lines of both these faults are made
conspicuous across the country by the fact that steep-sided valleys have been carved out along them. This testifies to the degree
to which the movement along them broke up the rocks and has
made them more susceptible to erosion.

Aberystwyth Grits

The Aberystwyth Grits formation provides splendid rock-exposures, and is fully and spectacularly displayed along the coast. In these exposures there are to be seen the clearest possible examples of fundamental geological facts and of the obvious inferences to be drawn from them. As to these, explanation is simple; but at the same time these rocks pose many intriguing questions that are by no means easy to answer. We shall therefore look at this formation rather closely; and especially as it lies at the front door of a flourishing university geological department, forms the foundation of a large town, and is walked over every year by thousands of holiday-makers.

The crescent-shaped outcrop is shown on our map. We must keep in mind that the geological map of Cardiganshire would extend to the west into Cardigan Bay and beyond if the sea and sediments accumulating there were cleared away. Thus the Aberystwyth Grits would then presumably have something of an elliptical outcrop. This is truncated, more or less along its length, by the coast, so we see only the eastern part of it. The coastal truncation extends for about 26 miles from 2 miles south of Borth to 4 miles south of New Quay. The maximum width of outcrop is about 8 miles.

The boundary of the outcrop of the Aberystwyth Grits is not easy to map with any precision, partly because it is not possible to draw a sharp line between the typical 'gritty' lithology of that formation and the predominantly shaly lithology of the surrounding formation, and also because of confusion due to rapidly changing dips, with folds and faults. If the boundary were to be clearly detected anywhere it would be in the clean-cut cliff sections. But it is by no means conspicuous even here, because of this kind of structural confusion; neither at the north end, south of Borth, nor at its south end, south of New Quay. Therefore it is no surprise to find that we can define its inland boundary only approximately.

Assuming the formation to represent a particular period of time, the elliptical occurrence at the surface (the crescent-shaped land outcrop together with its presumed continuation beneath the sea) would indicate a syncline or elongated trough whose axis lay a mile or two out in Cardigan Bay. The uppermost (newest) beds would lie in the central part of this structural trough.

Graptolites are to be found sporadically throughout the Aberystwyth Grits, though they are not well preserved and so are usually difficult to identify specifically. The assemblage indicates the zone of *Monograptus turriculatus*. This index-species itself has often been described as common, although no undoubted specimens of it have turned up during the fairly thorough collecting carried out during the last fifty years. However, one of the commonest forms in these rocks, also characteristic of the *turriculatus* zone, appears to be *Monograptus spiralis* which is not very unlike *M. turriculatus*, particularly in rather poorly-preserved specimens on the flattened shale. This species does not appear in the published lists and so there may be confusion as to identification here.

It has been suggested (by O. T. Jones) that at the south end of the outcrop, south of New Quay, the basal beds of the Aberystwyth Grits belong to the lowest part of the *turriculatus* zone, but that at the north end, south of Borth, the basal beds belong to the very top of that zone, if not even to the succeeding zone of *Monograptus crispus*. The question therefore arises as to whether the base of the Aberystwyth Grits formation is diachronous; that is whether, instead of representing a time-plane, it represents a later time in the north than in the south. The latter case would mean that the kind of sedimentation which has given rise to the characteristic lithology of the formation began earlier in the south than in the north. This kind of question is one of the most important in the whole of geology. Putting it in a general form, it is this: to what extent does any particular mappable formation, a formation easily recognisable in the field by its lithological character, truly represent, exactly and everywhere, one particular period of time? As a preliminary assumption we took this to be so in the case of the Aberystwyth Grits; but we now see there is a doubt about it.

This brings up the whole matter of facies. During any period of time it is only natural to suppose that sediments of one kind are being deposited over one area of deposition while other kinds are being deposited over neighbouring areas. Thus the rocks representing that period of time over a whole region will be of correspondingly varying lithological type.

Rocks lithologically similar to the Aberystwyth Grits occur in two other separated outcrops: (1) in Cwm Ystwyth and east of the Teifi valley in the neighbourhood of Tregaron, a region of Cardiganshire some 15 miles south-east of Aberystwyth; and (2) in the Tarannon and Talerddig neighbourhood in Montgomeryshire, some 25 miles north-east of Aberystwyth. These two easterly outcrops lie along the axis of the Central Wales syncline. The three outcrops have usually been taken to be parts of one continuous formation separated by folding and subsequent erosion. But the rocks of these three outcrops may not be parts, now separated by erosion, of a once-continuous grit-formation; they may represent areas of deposition of a 'gritty' facies that were originally separate. It may be that the Aberystwyth Grits formation is the same age as (not younger than) the predominantly shaly rocks to the east; in any case they both belong to the Ystwyth stage.

We now examine some details of the primary features of the formation and it will be found that these are of the greatest interest.

As already stated, the characteristic lithology is an alternation of shaly and gritty beds (figs 38, 39), the pale grit beds showing conspicuous 'ribbon-banding' on a more or less smoothed surface. The individual grit beds vary in thickness from a fraction of an inch to several feet.

In nearly every case a grit bed is coarser at the bottom than at the top. Looking at a cleanly exposed rock-surface we notice that the trace, on this surface, of the bottom of a grit bed is more sharply defined than that of the top, the grit passing gradually up into shaly mudstone. One grit bed and its passage into the overlying mudstone thus exhibits graded bedding. The particular bedding sequence in the Aberystywth Grits is thus, starting at the bottom of a grit bed: relatively coarse-grained base sharply marked off from the underlying mudstone, decrease in coarseness upwards, gradual passage into mudstone, the mudstone keeping its uniform very fine-grained character until it is abruptly succeeded by the next grit bed. (This sequence is a generalisation of what is observed; there is plenty of variation.)

A very useful structural test is provided by the above sequence. Strata may be locally overturned, and it might not be easy to say whether this were so or not, particularly in an isolated exposure. But applying our generalisation, derived of course from sequences where we are confident that the beds are the original way up, we should detect (or at least strongly suspect) overturning if we found that it was the upper surfaces of the grit beds, not the lower, that were the sharply defined ones.

This illustrates the importance of noting details in our geological observations in the field; details, such as we have here, that at first might not seem particularly worthy of note. It is of special interest to us in this case, as it was here, at the foot of the Aberystwyth cliffs, that Edward Bailey in 1930 first pointed out how the detailed reading of a bedding sequence could be used in reading the 'way up' of strata in doubtful cases.

Stratification within a grit bed may be fairly uniform, and parallel, but very often part of it may be highly convoluted. The lateral extension of the individual grit beds varies greatly. Along some parts of the coast all these beds, even the thinnest ones, and thus the whole vertical stratal pattern, can be traced with practically constant thickness for remarkably long distances— for half a mile or so; the tracing of the continuity only being halted, in many cases, by faults and other disturbances which prevent the recognition of individual beds beyond the disturbance. At other places the grit beds are seen to thin and wedge out.

The mudstone beds tend to show some degree of slaty cleavage as well as original shaly lamination. The presence of the frequent grit beds prevented any good development of this structure when the lateral pressure was applied.

Curious objects in the rocks, which must be considered as part of the lithology, are the nodules, concretions of flattened spherical shape, in size from an inch or two to a foot or more across (fig 40). The material composing them seems to be much the same as the ordinary grit, but there is probably a greater proportion of iron. When split across the middle a small core of pure pyrite, iron sulphide, is sometimes found. A special feature is the cone-in-cone structure of the outer parts. The cones point inwards, have annular grooves and fit one into another. These cake-like objects are rather hard, often weathering conspicuously and falling out of the rocks in which they are embedded. They are especially common in the northern part of the outcrop, both along the coast and inland. Though rather

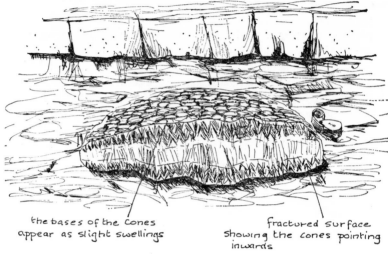

the bases of the Cones
appear as slight swellings

fractured surface
showing the cones pointing
inwards

Fig 40   A cone-in-cone concretion in the Aberystwyth Grits

characteristic of the Aberystwyth Grits they are by no means peculiar to this formation in the British sequence. Their origin is obscure, but some kind of a percolation and crystallisation process seems to be involved. Nor is it clear exactly when they were formed in relation to the sedimentation.

Specially interesting features of the Aberystwyth Grits are the sole-marks which occur on the under surfaces of the grit beds (fig 41). These are the marks, striations, little ridges and protuberances, etc, which are usually to be considered as the counterparts, the moulds, of corresponding marks, grooves, and dents made on the surface of the underlying mud before the covering coarser sediment was laid down. These 'negatives', being in relief on a hard surface, are more likely to be preserved, and to be conspicuous, than the original intaglio 'positives', even though we have to find exposed, and examine, the under sides (the 'soles') of these hard beds.

The commonest sole-marks are evidently those mentioned above, being the result of any special details of the sedimentation process. Various forms of this kind of sole-mark have been recognised, but attempts to classify and name them according to their supposed mode of origin have not so far been very satisfactory.

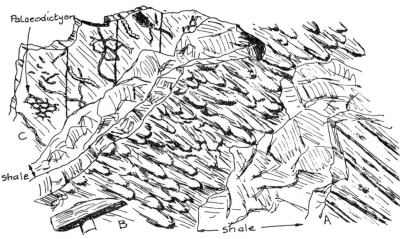

Fig 41 Vertical grits, showing sole-marks, on the foreshore
north of Clarach

The most intriguing marks are those that seem to have been
made, or may possibly have been made, by the activities of
living animal organisms. If so made they are trace-fossils (fig
41). The commonest are the winding ridges which almost certainly represent the tracks of some kind of invertebrate crawler;
they are often called 'worm-tracks', but the animal might have
been a snail, for example. (All the invertebrate animal phyla
had been evolved by these early Silurian times.) A more striking
pattern is the polygonal net-like structure, with the individual
meshes about an inch or so across, often called by the generic
name *Palaeodictyon*, as if there was no doubt as to its organic
nature. But this structure is altogether problematical.

Thirdly there are the sole-marks of tectonic origin, due to the
relative movement of contiguous surfaces during the folding of
the rocks as a whole. The fine parallel striations seen on many
of the smoother surfaces are doubtless of this nature. These
parallel 'slip-scratches' are a case of slickenside markings, the
ordinary slickensides being produced along faults which break
across the rocks. What appear to be a special manifestation of
the slip-scratch phenomenon are curious curved, angular, and
zig-zag marks on some of the bedding surfaces at a few places
along the cliffs. These indicate correspondingly irregular movements.

The conditions and manner of sedimentation of the Aberystwyth Grits are not very definitely indicated by the facts we can observe today in the resultant rocks, though these matters have been considered in detail by Wood and Smith who have thrown much light on the problems involved. The depth of water is uncertain but the area of deposition cannot have been very far from land. Subsidence must have been fairly fast to accommodate the great thickness of deposits. The intermittent deposition of gritty sediment was probably due to heavily turbid currents every now and then suddenly starting to flow down the marginal slopes of the basin. The graded bedding effect can easily be visualised as being due to a sudden influx of a mixture of rock-particles of all sizes, the larger tending to settle first. The irregularities and convolutions in the bedding of the grits indicate a forward movement of the currents, which seem to have come from a southerly direction.

The Aberystwth Grits formation provides examples of geological phenomena of a kind entirely different from those primary features we have been considering. These are the secondary tectonic structures imposed in the rocks by subsequent lateral pressures at the end of the Silurian period. We have already mentioned the fact that the rocks are highly folded and broken by many faults. Examples of the smaller-scale folds and faults are to be seen to the greatest perfection—in section, plan, and relief—all along the coast (and in some places inland). These are, of course, phenomena of the very first importance in geology, and it is not likely that there would be found in any other part of the world a better display than we have here of every conceivable kind of structure. It would need a large book to do justice to these beautiful exhibits, and to all the fundamental general facts and principles they illustrate. Here we shall have to be content with a few representative examples shown in our sketches (figs 38, 39, 43). But they must be seen *in situ*.

Very conveniently, an excellent selection may be examined by walking along the three-quarters of a mile of rocky shore between Aberystwyth and Clarach Bay to the north. When planning this, it is absolutely essential to start from the Aberystwyth end and at a time when the tide is falling, with the water about two-thirds of the way out. Otherwise the walker, only too likely

to be absorbed and delayed by the attractions of the almost inexhaustible geological phenomena to be observed, may find himself cut off by the tide.

The vast majority of the deformation structures were quite
clearly formed in the way and at the time we have mentioned.
But there are some crumplings of the strata that might possibly
have been caused by sliding and slumping very soon after they
had been deposited. There are, also, other appearances along
the coast of foldings and contortions of the strata which are of
superficial and extremely recent origin—indeed, they are no
doubt now and always in process of formation—being due to
the movement under gravity of loosened rock, but still with
something of the bedding intact, down the steep slope.

The Pont-erwyd district

The region between Plynlimon and Devil's Bridge, centred on
the village of Pont-erwyd, is the one region of Cardiganshire of
which the geology has been worked out in detail (fig 42). This
was done by O. T. Jones during the early years of this century
and the results were published in 1909 in a famous paper in the
Geological Society's *Quarterly Journal*. This must always remain
the most important single contribution to our knowledge of the
geology of the county and, indeed, it inaugurated a new era in
the investigation of the geological wilderness of Central Wales.
This was soon followed by similar work on the Machynlleth
district, by Jones and Pugh, published in the *Quarterly Journal*
for 1915. It was with acute geological foresight that Jones chose
this Pont-erwyd district for detailed research, as it is not likely
that any other small area of the county would have yielded such
important results.

The area lies astride the axis of the southward-plunging Plynlimon anticline (anticlinorium), so that the lowest rocks are
found in the centre of the north part and the highest towards
the south-west and south-east corners. It should be noted that if
the successive rock strata were arranged fairly horizontally, the
higher rocks would of course be found on the higher ground,
that is, here, on Plynlimon; but of the two factors determining
outcrop, relief and structure, structure is here the governing one.

The rocks of the Plynlimon stage contain few fossils; such as
there are indicate the zone of *Dicellograptus anceps*, the top

H

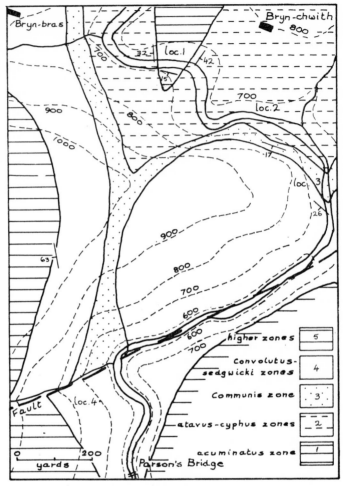

Fig 42   Geological map of the Rheidol Gorge section, south of
Pont-erwyd (*after O. T. Jones, 1909*)

zone of the Ordovician Bala series.

The Pont-erwyd stage is highly fossiliferous, with graptolites
beautifully preserved, often in full relief in pyrite. These have
enabled the strata to be discriminated into zones which fit into
the general detailed zonal scale of this part of the Silurian (see
Appendix). Although the outcrop is relatively narrow, the stage
comprises the whole series of zones from the *Glyptograptus per-*

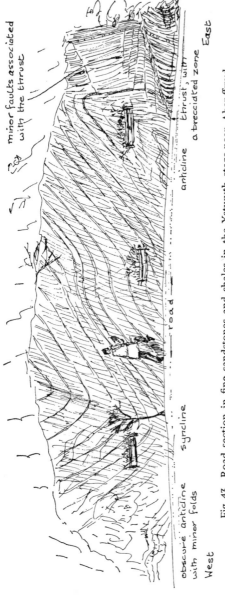

Fig 43 Road section in fine sandstones and shales in the Ystwyth stage near Aber-ffrwd

sculptus zone at the bottom to the *Monograptus sedgwicki* zone at the top.

The Ystwyth stage has not been satisfactorily subdivided. Graptolites are not plentiful but all the rocks appear to belong to the one zone of *Monograptus turriculatus*.

In our sketch-map of the district the strata are shown grouped as follows:

5. Ystwyth stage.
4. Zones of *M. convolutus* to *M. sedgwicki*.
3. Zones of *M. triangulatus* to *M. leptotheca* (collectively called by Jones the zone of *M. communis*).
2. Zones of *M. atavus* to *M. cyphus*
1. Zones of *Glyptograptus persculptus* to *Akidograptus acuminatus*.

To note some particulars of this most interesting area let us take an itinerary through a representative part of it.

The itinerary should begin on the bridge at Pont-erwyd where the A44 road from Aberystwyth crosses the river Rheidol, moving thence 300yd back up the road to the front of the George Borrow Hotel. From both places we see the glacial diversion to be mentioned in our next section. Strong vertical jointing is conspicuous in the *Monograptus convolutus* beds of the ravine just opposite the hotel. We shall pass over land with a variety of ownership and authority, so it is imperative to proceed discreetly, carefully avoiding any negligence or damage.

Our route takes the cartroad from the hotel, over the bridge across the stream, through a gate and up round the shoulder of a hillside with a view of the diversion from its south side. As we reach the brow of the hill the view opens out to the south and we see the other glacial diversion, the so-called 'incised meander'. Beyond it is a conspicuous cliff in the jointed *convolutus* beds, and we may be able to make out something of the main anticlinal structure in the rocks above and to the right of this cliff.

We pass through the farmyard of Bryn-bras, step over (or possibly have to walk through) a stream, and cross over a boggy field to a gate. Beyond this the cartroad becomes an indistinct track bearing up the hillside to the right, and we leave it to make our way obliquely down the slope to the river.

Near the bottom, at locality 1 on our map (fig 42), we can see the crest of the main anticline (as the whole structure proves it to be) in the far bank of the river. Here beds of the *Monograptus atavus* zone are exposed. On the whole, our route through the gorge traverses an upward succession of zones. If the condition of the river allows it, it is worth while going some 200yd upstream to the bend, where two sharp folds (in the atavus beds) are beautifully exposed in plan. These plunge to the south, in accordance with the general structure. Continuing downstream fossils are not readily to be found until we have walked under the vertical cliff and on to a shelf of ground along an old mineleet. Here (locality 2) the river is running eastwards and the rocks dip south-westwards. Extensive bedding surfaces, weathering purplish brown, are laid bare along the leet, and many graptolites are seen on them. Long forms, particularly the species *Monograptus acinaces* (the name *M. rheidolensis* used by Jones is a synonym), are the most striking, though *Climacograptus törnquisti* is the commonest species.

If the river is low it is just possible to follow the leet round the corner, but otherwise climb a little way up the bank and drop down 100yd farther on. Here (locality 3) is another shelf by the river, stretching for about 50yd. Fossils can be readily collected, particularly from the *Monograptus triangulatus* zone. Excellently preserved graptolites occur in several bands of dark shale separated by less fossiliferous paler mudstones.

The commonest fossil here is again *Climacograptus törnquisti*. Slightly less abundant are the forms of *Monograptus* comprised within the variation series *M. fimbriatus—M. triangulatus*. The specific nomenclature is unfortunate as *M. fimbriatus* has blunt triangular thecae while *M. triangulatus*, particularly in its more extreme form, has long separated tubular thecae approaching the *Rastrites* type. At this locality there is a band in which the cephalopod *Orthoceras* and other 'shelly' fossils may be found. *Monograptus communis* is also frequent, together with a number of other species of the genus and also biserial species of *Diplograptus* type (a 'wide' genus that includes *Orthograptus*, *Glyptograptus*, and *Mesograptus*), *Petalograptus*, and *Rastrites*. At locality 2 only *Monograpti* with simple thecae occur, while at this locality those with more or less curved and hooked thecae predominate. We have thus witnessed a general evolution within the genus. The ledge ends southwards in a quite inaccessible little ravine into which the river plunges. Here may be seen many small well-rounded potholes.

From this point we have to scramble up a steep bank for about 100ft and cut through a little rocky escarpment to our left. The river follows a straight course south-eastwards for about half a mile and the mapping shows that this is the line of a large fault along which, as being a line of weakness, the river has carved its valley. This expression of the fault line is continued in the gully of a small tributary as the river swings away in a more southerly direction. We make our way down the slope and through a wood until we drop on to the leet forming, in effect, a convenient path with the river 100ft precipitously below. Old mine workings are soon reached (locality 4) and specimens of ores, chiefly zinc blende, may be picked up. The leet ends at the mine but a path continues to lead down to Parson's Bridge. From this path and the bridge itself a splendid series of potholes is seen in the river-bed.

From the bridge a path zig-zags up the steep valley-side on the farther (eastern) side of the valley. When the slope eases off an interesting view unfolds to the south. The most striking feature is the steep V-shaped valley deeply entrenched in the floor of a wide-open valley. A mile and a half to the south the Rheidol makes a sharp and permanent turn to the west, flowing down a gradually widening valley to the sea. The line of the open valley is seen to continue directly southwards through a dip in the skyline, which is known to be largely filled with drift. Did the Rheidol once flow through that valley and has it been diverted to the west at Devil's Bridge by river capture? Or was the present Rheidol above Devil's Bridge, where we have been following it southwards, originally a tributary to a main river flowing westwards, now represented by the Mynach and lower Rheidol? Argument and speculation will doubtless arise and the discussion may be renewed later at Devil's Bridge, as we stand on the terrace in front of the Hafod Arms Hotel. From this point the famous view extends northwards up the incised Rheidol valley, backed on the skyline by the waved crest of the lower of the two humps of Plynlimon. Structurally, we are looking directly along the axis of the southward plunging main Plynlimon anticline. (An account of this itinerary was published in the *Amateur Geologist* in 1968.)

The Ice Age

During the Ice Age northern Cardiganshire was covered by ice, mainly that radiating outwards from Plynlimon and the other high ground of the Plynlimon range. In the north-west corner of the country this ice moving westwards, was joined by ice coming from the mountains to the north, particularly by that coming from the upper part of the Dyfi valley. This spread several miles inland from the coast about as far south as Aberystwyth, as shown by the presence of boulders of felsite of a type found particularly in the Aran range. Somewhere a little south of the present village of Aberarth the Irish Sea ice, which had already overridden Anglesey and Lleyn, encroached some way onto the landward side of the coast, joining the more locally derived ice.

Towards the end of the period of glaciation the ice flowing westwards, which came from the mountain country of north Cardiganshire, began to withdraw inland while the belt of ground along the coastal area to the south of the Dyfi estuary was still occupied by ice which had travelled down that estuary (as mentioned above). Between a mile or two south of Machynlleth and a mile or so north-east of Aberystwyth all the streams draining westward were therefore blocked at their lower ends by ice, and it is very likely that in these valleys lakes were impounded which escaped southwards over various cols. This idea is supported by the presence of notches and dry channels cut across the inter-valley ridges (fig 44). This neat picture may be too simple, and some of these deserted channels may have been produced by streams flowing along the margin of the Dyfi glacier.

In some cases the streams were permanently diverted. For instance, the Leri, instead of now flowing through what was presumably its pre-glacial exit north of Talybont, turns through a right angle south of the village and flows through a gorge to Borth. Here it is impeded from quite a different cause, as it has been diverted to flow into the Dyfi estuary by the growth northwards of the shingle ridge (encouraged by man-made channelling) between Borth and Ynys-las.

Small-scale but striking looped diversions of the Rheidol occur at Pont-erwyd, one just below the hotel and two others, one half

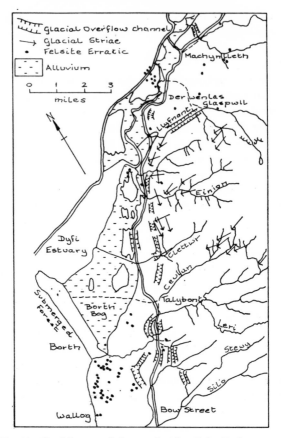

Fig 44   Glacial map of the south side of the Dyfi estuary
(*after Jones and Pugh, 1935*)

a mile above, and the other half a mile below, the village. The
deserted direct channels remain blocked with boulder-clay. Two
of these we have observed in our itinerary through that district.

As in Snowdonia and the Cader Idris range we have in northern Cardiganshire, and particularly in neighbouring parts of
Montgomeryshire and Merioneth, corries caused by the scooping action of the ice on the mountain-sides. Although the relief
in these purely sedimentary rocks was, and is, gentler than in
those other regions composed largely of igneous rocks, there
are several large steep-walled corries which make very marked

features in the mountain topography. Travelling along the road from Aberystwyth to Machynlleth we see several on the hills to the north of the Dyfi estuary, particularly on Tarren Hendre. South of the Dyfi in the wild mountain country north of Plynlimon are several fine corries, notably those of Tarren Bwlchgwyn, and the heads of the Hengwm and Llyfnant valleys. Each of these has a cascading stream which adds to the scenic attractions of these remote places. The only corrie in these rocks that contains a lake is a small one just to the north of the main summit of Plynlimon, where we have Llyn Llygad-Rheidol, the main head-waters of the Aberystwyth water-supply.

The material relics of the Ice Age are the deposits carried, laid down, and left behind by the ice and its associated waters. Very widespread is the boulder-clay, often with intercalated gravels and sands. This is conspicuous in innumerable inland exposures, for instance in the road-cuttings and stream-banks in the more upland parts, with typically subangular and striated boulders of all sizes. The largest of these boulders occur as 'erratics' scatered over the countryside; these have usually been moved by the farmer to less inconvenient spots at the edges of his fields.

The most striking of the occurrences of these deposits are those where the glacial material is still plastered against the present sea-cliffs or forms low-lying plains in front of the slopes of the pre-glacial coastline, as between Llanrhystyd and Llansantffraid (Llanon). Some of the cliffs carved in boulder-clay are vertical, with eroded gullies and pinnacles, as at Morfa Bychan (fig 45). It is obvious that all this glacial material still left along the coast is being rapidly worn away.

Some accumulations of superficial material in regions that have been subjected to the rigours of the Ice Age may have been formed not by the ice itself but as a result of the cold frosty conditions surrounding the ice-margin and for a time prevailing over the region after the total disappearance of the ice. These are 'periglacial' conditions. Such may be the origin of some of the features here, particularly some of the larger screes and the tumbled masses of rock-debris seen, for instance, in Cwm Ystwyth.

A feature of the beaches which attracts not only the geologist but the casual visitor is the variety of coloured and speckled

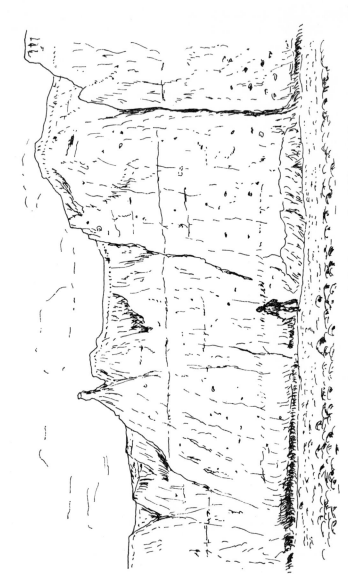

Fig 45 Cliffs in boulder-clay at Morfa Bychan, south of Aberystwyth

pebbles among the shingle, as for instance at Aberystwyth at the north end of the promenade and on the Tan-y-bwlch beach. The geologist at once recognises most of these as being igneous rocks that have come far. As the general drift of shore material is towards the north we might have expected to find the 'parent' rocks somewhere to the south. But it turns out that they can be matched only by rocks to the north. The pebbles of flint, which are common, can hardly have come from anywhere but the Chalk of Antrim in Ireland; though concealed Chalk areas beneath the Irish Sea are a possible source. However, all this can be readily explained when we visualise the Irish Sea ice depositing its 'boulders' at the southern end of its extension, somewhere in St George's Channel, whence they have been washed up onto the shore to the north-east and worn into the shapes typical of beach pebbles.

Geomorphology

Northern Cardiganshire provides a splendid variety of landforms of all kinds, shapes, and sizes, and excellent opportunities for the study of fundamental principles in geomorphology, many of which are by no means fully understood.

The important question as to the way in which the hill-top surface has been produced arises here as it does in all upland hill districts. We have already considered the question as it applies to Snowdonia. Here, in northern Cardiganshire, there has been and still is much speculation about this matter.

According to one view this imaginary surface is made up of two or three essentially separate plateaus. According to another view it is one perfectly continuous, gently curved surface. These two views as to the form of the surface correspond to two quite different interpretations of its nature and history.

Those who claim to see several plateaus interpret them as separately uplifted plains of marine erosion. The present writer holds the second view to be the correct one. According to this the hill-top surface is one carved by sub-aerial erosion out of an uplifted region, its form being the very flattened expression of the general curve of erosion. The smoothness of this hill-top surface, particularly the plateau quality of its higher parts, is then taken to be due to the generally rather uniform character of the rocks. The uplifted region, if it ever reached the height to which earth-movement alone would have carried it, would have been hundreds, if not thousands, of feet above the present hill-top surface.

It seems that the present disposition of the features of the re-lief can be to a considerable extent explained on the simple principle of the differential erosion of the harder and softer Lower Palaeozoic rocks. Thus the dominant physical feature of the county, the mountain of Plynlimon, seems clearly to be due to the rocks of Upper Ordovician age, harder than the average for the district, becoming exposed by erosion in the core of the Plynlimon structural dome.

The detailed correspondence between rock-outcrop and sur-face-feature is everywhere to be seen in small escarpments. In the Pont-erwyd district, here and there, they serve to emphasise the structure of folds plunging to the south. Perhaps the most striking correspondence between relief and structure is that pro-vided by the course of the Llyfnant and Ystwyth faults along which deep straight valleys have been carved, as mentioned in our section on the structure.

'Beauty spots' are not always those that intrigue the mind

Fig 46   The 'submerged forest' at Borth

as well as the eye. But Devil's Bridge is one of those that do. We have referred to the river features here in our itinerary through the gorge of the Rheidol.

The coast of Cardiganshire may be said to be generally a rather high one; that is, the features produced by marine erosion (the sea-cliff and the slope induced above it) extend up into the general surface of the land which stands, just along the coast, at about 400ft above the sea. This seems to be readily explained on the supposition that here, in the centre of Cardigan Bay, the

Fig 47 Coastal erosion (*from a photograph taken about 1936*)

sea has cut relatively far into a land mass having a general slope
to the west.

The details of the physiography of shore and cliff are very
clearly controlled by the disposition of the beds (the direction of
dip in relation to the trend of the coast, and the steepness of
dip) and by other structural features, especially joints and, to
a less extent, faults (figs 47-50).

Fig 48   The fallen Egg Rock (*from a photograph taken by A. Wood
about 1956*)

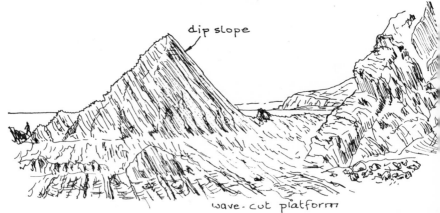

Fig 49   Craig y Filfran, the Cormorant Rock

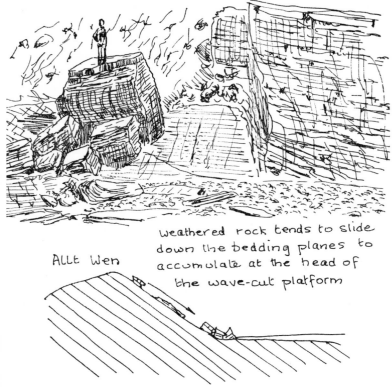

weathered rock tends to slide
down the bedding planes to
accumulate at the head of
the wave-cut platform

Allt Wen

Fig 50 The cliffs at Allt Wen, south of Aberystwyth

A comparatively recent sinking of the land relative to the sea seems to be strongly suggested, if not actually proved, by the position of the solid rock-floor well below sea-level in, for instance, the Dyfi estuary. The well known 'submerged forest' between Borth and Ynys-las, recently extensively exposed, is evidence of encroachment by the sea but not necessarily of subsidence of the land.

Sources

A detailed review of geological research in Cardiganshire from the time when that was begun (*c* 1842) until the end of 1967 has been made by the present writer (1969). The most important written works published during that time were those of Jones

(1909, 1912, 1922, 1938), those of Jones and Pugh (1915, 1935), and that of Wood and Smith (1958). We have also mentioned the historically intersting paper by Keeping (1881). Since 1967 the following, among others, have appeared: Bassett's structural review (1969); Watson's accounts of features connected with the Ice Age (1969, 1970); Lovell's investigation of lateral variations within the Aberystwyth Grits (1970); a study of the Ordovician rocks of the Plynlimon outcrop by James (1971); and a discussion of certain deformation structures near Aberystwyth by Fitches (1972). In the third edition of the Regional Geology handbook of South Wales (George, 1970), northern Cardiganshire is given considerable attention.

The occurrence and composition, industrial history, and methods of working of the mineral lodes of north Cardiganshire and west Montgomeryshire form a large subject which is hardly within our scope. These matters, particularly the history, are discussed with references by North (1962), treated in great detail by Lewis (1967), and given a short summary in Lewis's entertaining book (1970). From the geological standpoint the Geological Survey memoir by Jones (1922) is the one full and authoritative work.

CHAPTER 11

North-East Wales

The wide areas of country—roughly the counties of Denbigh and Flint—that constitute the north-eastern parts of North Wales are less dramatic in their scenery than the rugged counties of Caernarvon and Merioneth to the west. The geology too is in a lower key, though any feeling of monotony among the dark highly folded Lower Palaeozoic rocks is dispelled by the sight of the light grey masses of Carboniferous Limestone riding here and there to the east like ships on a rough sea. Such are the Ormes Heads and the Eglwyseg Rocks near Llangollen. And on the extreme eastern edge we have the North Wales Coalfield where mineral wealth is brought into the service of man, with the corresponding industrial scene being the chief feature of the landscape.

Succession

Triassic	New Red Sandstone
Carboniferous	Coal Measures Millstone Grit Carboniferous Limestone
Silurian	Ludlow Wenlock Llandovery
Ordovician	Upper Bala (Ashgill) Lower Bala (Caradoc) Llandeilo

Structure

The geological structure is complicated in detail but the following generalisations can be made.

The Lower Palaeozoic rocks, ranging from the Llandeilo (a very little, in the middle of the dome structure of the Berwyn Hills) through the Lower and Upper Bala, Llandovery, Wenlock,

J

and Ludlow, were deformed—folded, faulted, and cleaved—as part of the general deformation of the Lower Palaeozoic rocks of North Wales at some time soon after the end of the Silurian period. The general alignment of the structure is, however, in these north-easterly parts in a direction east and west, rather than north-east to south-west as in the other parts of North Wales.

Carboniferous rocks enter very largely into the structure of the most northerly and easterly parts and lie unconformably on the eroded surface of the underlying Lower Palaeozoic rocks. This unconformity separates two sets of formations, the Lower Palaeozoic and the Carboniferous sets, which have structures that are, in the first place, entirely independent the one from the other; but the post-Carboniferous earth-movements imposed additional structures on both sets together. The most structurally conspicuous—and the most scenically conspicuous—of these super-imposed tectonic structures are certain large faults which are found (as a result, of course, of geological mapping) to cut right across both the Lower Palaeozoic and the Carboniferous formations. The movement along these faults was mostly along the direction of the fault (strike-slip) rather than up-and-down the fault surface (dip-slip); that is, they are largely wrench (tear) faults. The largest of these faults are in the Llangollen area. The Carboniferous rocks are thrown into gentle folds and the underlying Lower Palaeozoic rocks must have taken part in this folding, but such comparatively slight effects are difficult to detect among the much more violent earlier folding of the Lower Palaeozoics. Nor is it always possible to say whether those faults which are confined to the Lower Palaeozoic rocks are of end-of-Silurian age or end-of-Carboniferous age.

Not only is there a profound unconformity at the base of the Carboniferous, but the lapse of time it represents extends about halfway through the period during which the Carboniferous Limestone series as a whole was being deposited. This is shown by the fact that the lowest part of the Limestone, immediately overlying the unconformity, contains fossils (corals and brachiopods) characteristic of the upper part of that series, the *Dibunophyllum* zone.

The newest rocks in north-east Wales belong to the New Red Sandstone of Permo-Triassic age. These lie unconformably on all those older rocks on which they were deposited as loose materials after the completion of the end-of-Carboniferous movements and the consequent uplift and erosion.

The Llandudno and Colwyn Bay district

The Carboniferous Limestone of the coastal area of north-east Wales is most conspicuous in the neighbourhood of Llandudno and Colwyn Bay and particularly in those remarkable promontories, the Little Ormes Head and the Great Ormes Head. We mention the lesser one first as it is the first to come into view as the traveller from the North Midlands of England approaches by rail or road along the North Wales coast—and a very welcome and familiar sight it is to many.

The geology of the Ormes was described by Morton at the end of last century, and that of the Great Orme more fully by Smyth in 1925: The Little Orme and the Limestone around Colwyn Bay were described by Neaverson in 1937. An itinerary of the Great Orme is given in the recent guide to the Liverpool district by Bathurst and others.

The geological composition and structure of this little district is not only directly responsible for the interesting physical features of the land and coastline but it is also responsible for the other features of the scenery and the plant and animal life. The geology of a region is indeed a fundamental and integral part of its 'natural history'. To illustrate this, here is one of William Condry's graphic descriptions, from his book Exploring Wales.

We begin in a splendour of white cliffs, sea birds and wildflowers on that fine headland, the Great Orme at Llandudno. To see the wildflowers of the Orme at their best go in spring when vernal squill, hoary rockrose, spring cinquefoil and Nottingham catchfly are all flowering together. Note also the wild cabbage on those calcareous cliffs and you will understand why your garden brassicas do best in limy ground. Among sea birds the fulmar is a Great Orme speciality. Over the years Llandudno has done its best to tame the wildness of this 679ft Orme, a name that is a reminder of the Viking settlements of the ninth and tenth centuries. Yet the six miles of road cleverly engineered all round and the cable railway straight to the top have not deprived the Orme of being a place belonging to the sea and the wind rather than to a town. The Orme enjoys superb views west along the coast to Anglesey. East the coast stretches far away into Lancashire. Inland you look at the massive shoulders of the Carneddau. Three miles east a twin limestone promontory stands into the sea—the Little Orme, a wilder headland with no marine drive. It is another good place for sea birds, plants and breezy walks

Fig 51 The Great Orme from the coast near Penmaenmawr

along the edges of high white cliffs and above deep, abandoned quarries. Both Ormes, with Liverpool less than forty miles along the coast, are good perches for ship-watchers.

The Denbighshire Moors

Most of the north-western part of Denbighshire is composed of Silurian rocks of Wenlock and Ludlow age, collectively known as the Denbighshire Grits and Flags. The Wenlock strata can be distinguished from the Ludlow strata by means of the particular graptolites they contain (these graptolite fossils being well distributed throughout both series), but these two stratigraphical series together here form one thick and extensive unit of monotonous lithology, deformed as a whole by folding and faulting. 'Grits' predominate in the lower part, chiefly of Wenlock age, while 'flags' predominate in the upper part, chiefly of Ludlow age.

The Wenlock rocks outcrop over a curved band along the western and southern part of this area, forming a rim of what is, in a general way, a basin structure; but this structure is interfered with on its north-east side by the folds and faults of the Vale of Clwyd. Within the basin there are innumerable folds running on the whole east and west.

The distinctive relief and general scenery of this district, the Denbighshire Moors, results from the character and arrangement of the rocks.

In the northern part of Denbighshire few great high roads penetrate the Silurian districts of the country; the hills, rarely bold, but high and steep. are yet of incessant recurrence; and thus it is that to strangers it forms the least known district of North Wales. The ground is hilly in this sense only, that on a high table-land with an undulating surface, the rivers with all their numerous tributary rivulets have scooped out a great number of steep-sided valleys, which run hither and thither to every point of the compass. (Sir Andrew Ramsay, writing a hundred years ago in his great Memoir on North Wales).

West Denbighshire consists of a table-land which rises to a height of 1,750ft O.D. The plateau is perhaps best seen from viewpoints on the south of it, e.g. Garn Prys, near Pentre Voelas. The area is trenched by so many streams that in many districts it is dissected into isolated hills and ridges. Indeed, the common Welsh place-names, such as moel (rounded hill), mynydd (mountain), cefn (ridge), ffridd (mountain pasture) and craig (rocky eminence), bear witness to the repeated occurrence of characteristic topographic features. Where carpeted by heather or bracken, or covered by peat, the country offers little encouragement to the geologist seeking to elucidate the rock succession and structure, however fascinated he may be by the soothing and delicately-tinted panorama that unrolls before him. (Professor P. G. H. Boswell, who made a prolonged and detailed study of the 'Middle Silurian rocks of North Wales').

In many places parts of the succession, particularly where this is chiefly mudstone, have highly contorted bedding. These contorted beds (fig 52) may range in thickness from a foot or so up to about 100ft. A curious hummocky surface of the ground is pro-

Fig 52   A contorted bed about 3ft thick lying between evenly bedded sandstones and shales (after Boswell)

duced by the weathering and erosion of a thick contorted bed having a considerable width of outcrop. Professor O. T. Jones showed fairly conclusively in 1937 and 1939 that these greatly disturbed beds are the result of the sliding and slumping of mud under water as a part of the process of deposition on the sea floor during the Ludlow period, and that they now occur as contorted mudstones at various horizons in the general stratigraphical sequence of the Ludlow strata. This is proved chiefly by the character of the upper surfaces of these beds, between them and the overlying undisturbed beds. These surfaces are distinctly

marked, but they are uneven, the lowest layers of the horizontally deposited overlying beds filling in the irregularities and
being, as it were, now firmly 'welded' onto the top surfaces of
the disturbed beds. The surfaces are in a sense surfaces of unconformity, but the lowest layers of the undisturbed beds were
evidently deposited almost immediately after the sliding and
slumping of the underlying beds had stopped.

The alternative exlanation would be that the contortions and
crumplings are a part of the general deformation of the whole
series of rocks due to the end-of-the-Silurian earth-movements
and pressures; for some reasons (structural, dynamical) only
certain parts of the succession in certain areas being affected in
this violent way. But if this were so the contortions would either
pass gradually upwards, and downwards, into less affected strata
or there would be a clean-cut plane of separation (indicating
movement along the plane) at the top or bottom or both. This
phenomenon of slumping is best seen in the country extending
for about five miles south of Colwyn Bay.

The Vale of Clwyd and Clwydian Range

Of all the hill ranges of North Wales the Clwydian Range,
though of no great height, may be said to be the most distinct.
Geologically it is connected with the region of the Denbighshire
Moors to the west and much the same kind of relief and scenery
results from erosion of the same kind of rocks. But here
the Lower Palaeozoic (Ludlow) outcrop is relatively narrow and
separated from the West Denbighshire outcrop by the Carboniferous and Triassic rocks which (themselves largely overlain by
alluvium) form the beautiful and fertile Vale of Clwyd (fig 53).
On the east the Lower Palaeozoic rocks pass beneath the uncon-
formably-overlying easterly-dipping Carboniferous rocks of
which the Millstone Grit formation forms an escarpment south-
west of Mold.

The Clwydian Range is upstanding because the rocks composing it are hard and compacted by folding and are thus more
resistant to erosion than the rocks on each side of it. In saying
that it is a particularly distinct range one is recalling the attractive skyline as seen from the east, from the Wirral and the
Cheshire Plain. From the west side of the Vale of Clwyd the
range forms an imposing background to the view.

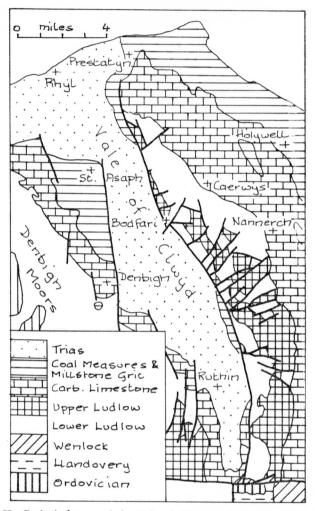

Fig 53 Geological map of the Vale of Clwyd and the Clwydian range
(*after Geological Survey*)

The main features of the geological structure of this region
deserve a careful examination because the problems that arise
here are typical of those in so many other British regions. Our
map shows the main outlines of the usual interpretation of
what can be seen of the outcrops on the ground and our section
(fig 54) shows one 'realisation' of the structure.

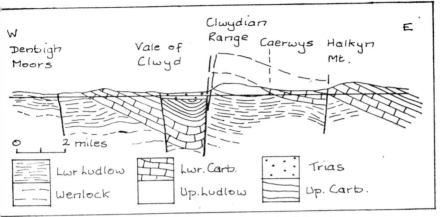

Fig 54   Geological section across the Vale of Clwyd
(*after Geological Survey*)

On the west side of the valley the Carboniferous and older rocks, and possibly the Triassic rocks as well, are traversed by faults oblique to the general trend of the Carboniferous outcrop and the direction of the valley. They may be considered as steps in the production of the western limb of the syncline of the Vale of Clwyd.

One of the most puzzling questions in British geology concerns the nature of the outcrop of the edge of the Trias where it abuts against older rocks to which in any case it would be unconformable. Is the boundary a fault or an undisturbed unconformity? The latter explanation, if it fits the facts, should logically be preferred until further information is forthcoming. The usual interpretation here, which is the one shown on our map (always remembering that most of the 'solid' geology is concealed beneath the superficial deposits) gives the Triassic rocks as being faulted; that is, the faulting is taken as having occurred after, not before, these rocks were laid down. But it is not clear whether the Triassic boundary is a faulted one or not.

There is the same uncertainty about the structure on the east side of the valley. Here a continuous fault is boldly drawn on the map, affecting at least the Carboniferous and Lower Palaeozoic rocks. There probably is a fault there, but even so it would be, essentially, merely a part of the eastern limb of the syncline.

Were these terrestrial Triassic deposits originally laid down

over part, perhaps even the whole, of the area now occupied
by the Lower Palaeozoic and Carboniferous outcrops? Was the
Trias of the Vale of Clwyd once continuous with the Trias of
Cheshire? If so, it was no doubt laid down over a very uneven
landscape of hill and dale, as we know that it must have been
elsewhere in Britain.

The Llangollen and Wrexham district
The whole of this district has been described in detail in the two
well-known Memoirs of the Geological Survey on the 'Country
around Wrexham', by C. B. Wedd and others, published in 1927
and 1928.

The following brief account of the district to the north of
Llangollen is selected from that given by L. J. Wills (one of the
authors of the Memoirs) for use during a field meeting of the
Geologists' Association in 1919.

The region (fig 55) lies among the eastern hills of Wales, where
they abut against the barrier range of Carboniferous rocks that
stands guardian over the rich Cheshire plains. Llangollen itself

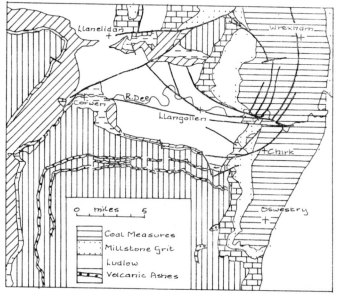

Fig 55 Geological map of the Llangollen area (*after Geological Survey*)

lies near the point where the Dee breaches the barrier, here weakened by the shattering of mighty faults.

As we look from near the town towards the north-east we see the wall of the Lower Carboniferous escarpment as an ordered background to the irregular but often flat-topped and steep-sided hills of Silurian rocks.

The Carboniferous strata strike almost north and south with a gentle dip to the east, and the great escarpment of the Limestones and Millstone Grit stretches away to the north of Llangollen with extreme regularity (fig 56). The part of the escarpment that we see from Llangollen is really produced by faults that throw the outcrop on the south side of the valley about two

Fig 56 The Eglwyseg scarp to the north of Llangollen
(*after Geological Survey*)

or three miles to the east. This belt of fracture can be traced right across the outcrop of the Carboniferous as one of the dominant structural features of the Ruabon Coalfield. To the south of the Dee valley and of these faults, the Limestone escarpment is much less conspicuous.

The Coal Measure outcrop follows that of the Millstone Grit to the east.

The Carboniferous Limestone rests unconformably on a gently undulating surface of Lower Palaeozoic rocks. In the hollows, lower beds occur, including red basement sandstones and conglomerates and a considerable thickness of limestone, which are elsewhere overlapped by the main mass of the limestone. This unconformity is a most striking feature on the map, because the general trend of the rocks below it is almost at right angles to the strike of the Carboniferous. It must be further pointed out that the surface of the unconformity has had imparted to it the dip of the Carboniferous, i.e. 5° or 10° towards the east. A small patch of Carboniferous Limestone at Corwen indicates that this formation formerly spread all over the Llangollen district.

To the south of Llangollen and the upper part of the Dee valley we have the structure of the Berwyn Dome which brings up the Ordovician Bala rocks over a roughly circular area some 15 miles across. These rocks are, on the whole, rather harder than the overlying Silurian so that a high hilly region corresponds to the dome structure. (We have seen the same thing, on a smaller scale, in the case of Plynlimon.) Intercalated in the sandy mudstones are beds of acidic volcanic ash (ignimbrites?), the thicker of which produce marked topographic features.

The extent of the Flintshire and Denbighshire coalfield is shown on our general map.

> The easterly regional dip causes the Carboniferous strata to plunge beneath the younger New Red Sandstone of the Cheshire plain; and it is probable that in this synclinal tract the Coal Measures of North Wales unite with those of the Lancashire and Staffordshire coalfields. In places boreholes have proved their occurence at depth; and vast amounts of unworked coal possibly lie buried in easternmost Denbighshire and Flintshire, though whether it lies near enough to the surface to be profitably exploited is not yet known. (George)

The Flintshire and Denbighshire coalfield is described by North in one of his incomparable works of geological exposition and explanation. Indeed, in his *Coal and the Coalfields of Wales* he discusses the whole natural history of coal.

It is needless to say that nowhere do we find a more intimate and obvious connexion between geology and man's activities than in the case of the coalfields.

CHAPTER 12

Anglesey

Anglesey impresses most casual visitors by its apparent flatness. This impression is reinforced by the view from the Snowdonian summits: in striking contrast to their rugged scenery the island of Anglesey (Môn), together with the lowlands of Arvon between Bangor and Caernarvon, appears to have a uniform height of about 2-300ft and the valleys cut into this surface are invisible. Above this level a few hills rise higher: Holyhead Mountain to 700ft, and, in an arc around the north and east coasts, Mynydd-y-garn, Parys Mountain, Mynydd Eilian, Mynydd Bodafon, Mynydd Llwydiarth and Bwrdd Arthur, all to about 500ft.

PRE-CAMBRIAN

The Pre-Cambrian rocks of Anglesey, named the Monian System by Blake in 1887 but more usually termed the Mona Complex, form the most extensive tract of ancient rocks in Britain south of the Scottish Highlands (fig 57). All the rocks were metamorphosed during an orogeny which appears to have occurred about 600 million years ago, just before the widespread appearance of animal life.

Succession
Because the rocks lack fossils, and also because of the metamorphism, the structure and succession of the Mona Complex are obscure. Greenly, in his large Memoir published in 1919, maintained that it comprised two suites of very different ages: (1) a very old 'basement' of highly metamorphosed gneisses; (2) a later 'bedded series' of marine sediments, with volcanic rocks at some horizons.

Shackleton, in 1969, described the gneisses as simply being the

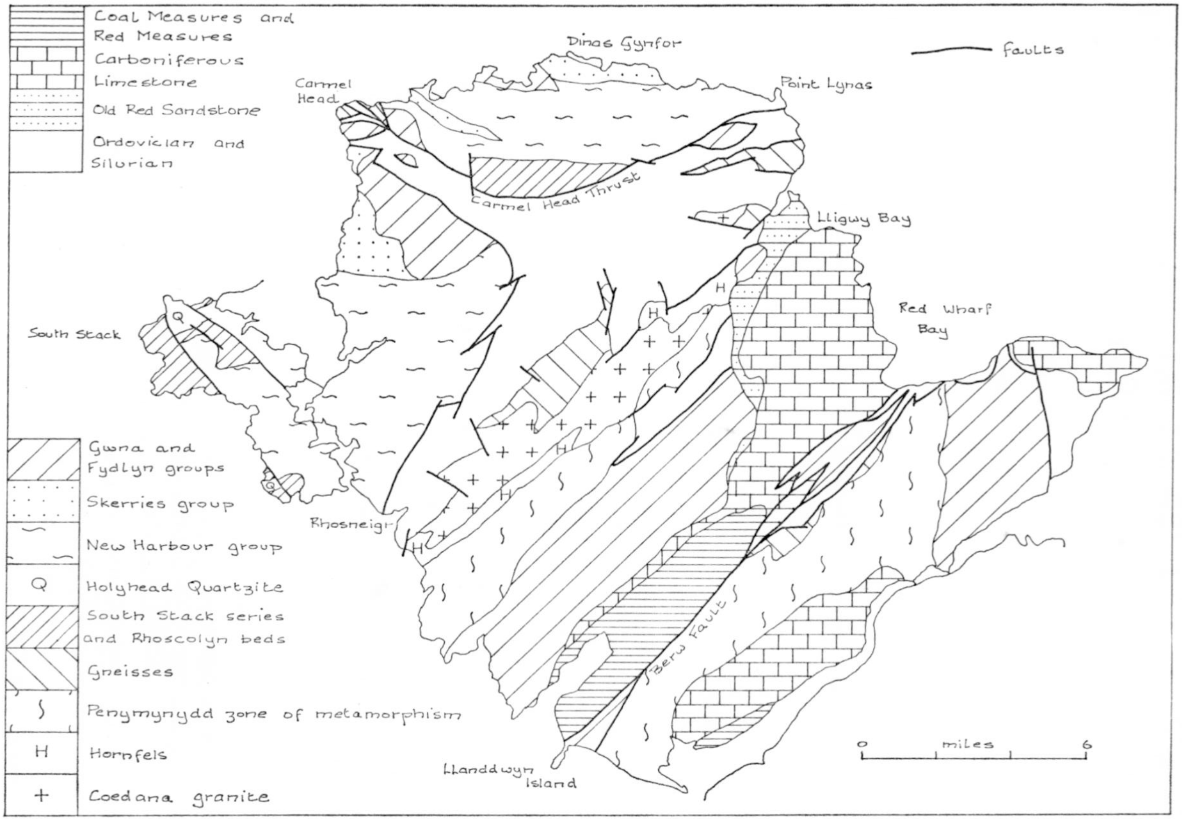

Fig. 57. Geological map of Anglesey (in part after Greenly)

Legend (upper block):
- Coal Measures and Red Measures
- Carboniferous Limestone
- Old Red Sandstone
- Ordovician and Silurian
- —— Faults

Legend (lower block):
- Gwna and Fydlyn groups
- Skerries group
- New Harbour group
- Q Holyhead Quartzite
- South Stack series and Rhoscolyn beds
- Gneisses
- ∽ Penmynydd zone of metamorphism
- H Hornfels
- + Coedana granite

Map labels:
Dinas Gynfor, Point Lynas, Carmel Head, Carmel Head Thrust, Lligwy Bay, Red Wharf Bay, South Stack, Rhosneigr, Berw Fault, Llanddwyn Island

0   miles   6

more highly metamorphosed portions of the bedded series, principally on the evidence of sedimentary structures preserved in
the less highly metamorphosed portions. This revised sequence
is as follows:

Fydlyn Felsitic group
Gwna group
Skerries group
New Harbour group
Rhoscolyn beds
Holyhead Quartzite
South Stack beds.

The total thickness was estimated by Greenly as being about
20,000ft.

Structure

In almost any outcrop the bedding of the fine-grained schistose
sedimentary rocks is seen to be twisted and contorted. Moreover, cleavage impressed on these rocks at an earlier time seems
itself to have been distorted (with further folding of the bedding,
which is often unrecognisable). One further feature of these
structures deserves emphasis. The folds appear to be 'plastic':
the impression is one of flowage of material, the rock being deformed as if it were putty. Fractures and faults, where seen,
appear to be later structures, the results of movement when the
rock was harder and more brittle. The complexity of the small-
scale folds suggests that the larger-scale structures are equally
complex, but these structures are not apparent in the field, and
can only be elucidated by very careful mapping of the rock-
types, and the study of the small-scale folds.

The largest folds which can be easily appreciated in the field
are those in the high cliffs at South Stack. These are in the
resistant South Stack beds, and the folds are (perhaps correspondingly) simpler than those of the schists. A striking feature of
the cliffs is the axial plane cleavage (fig 58).

Two interpretations have been given of the overall structure
of the Mona Complex, remarkably different from each other.
Greenly, on the evidence of the minor folding, and by analogy
with structures described from the Alps and Scotland, thought
of the major structures as being nappes or recumbent folds,
lying on their sides, rather like a series of blankets folded con-

Fig 58   Large upright folds with associated cleavage in grits of the
South Stack series at South Stack (*after Greenly, 1919*)

certina-wise. Shackleton, in contrast, believes that the major
structure is very simple, and that only one major anticline is
present (looking rather like one of the folds at South Stack), and
that its south-east limb is faulted repeatedly by the major faults
which cross the island.

South Stack beds

The South Stack beds are best known at South Stack, but can
be studied in coastal exposures (where the cliffs are accessible)
from North Stack to Porth-y-post, and also in the coast section
south-west of Rhoscolyn. Abundant evidence of 'way up' is provided in these beds, in which the original sedimentary structures
are often well preserved.

The beds form a typical greywacke suite, in which the greywackes form layers up to several feet thick, separated usually
by thin partings of mudstone, now a schist or phyllite. Conditions of deposition must have been very similar to those during
the deposition of the Aberystwyth Grits.

To see the South Stack beds one should descend the steps to
South Stack, preferably going across to the islet. The folds are
almost upright, slightly overturned to the south, which results

in the cleavage dipping at a high angle to the north (fig 58). Farther south the cliffs from Hen Borth to Porth Dafarch afford a chance to study a rather different type of folding—the folds have become isoclinal and overturned. The best and most easily accessible portion runs west of Porth Dafarch for nearly a mile. Similar folding is present at Rhoscolyn.

Holyhead Quartzite
Massive quartzites form the summit of Holyhead Mountain and the slope from there to North Stack. Bedding planes are very difficult to make out, and as a result the attitude of the beds is obscure. At Rhoscolyn the Holyhead Quartzite is thinner and more flaggy, and has split into two divisions, separated by greywackes.

Rhoscolyn beds
These beds are very similar to the South Stack beds. They may be seen at Borth Wen, south of Rhoscolyn, south and west of Holyhead, and between the base of the Holyhead breakwater and Porth Namarch. At many localities a thin band of green tuff intervenes between the Rhoscolyn beds and the succeeding New Harbour group: this is a useful marker horizon.

New Harbour group
These beds, principally of schists, are present in wide tracts in north and west Anglesey. Bands of bedded jasper and spilitic lavas are intercalated. The group is well exposed on the shore south-east of Rhoscolyn and around Tre-arddur Bay, but the most accessible section is between Salt Island and Soldier's Point, Holyhead. Other fine sections are seen on the mainland shore west of Llanfwrog. Flaggy schists are well exposed where they form the north coast of Anglesey, especially around Amlwch and Point Lynas.

Skerries group
The Skerries group marks a major volcanic episode in the deposition of the Mona Complex rocks. In general the rocks form sedimentary accumulations of volcanic material (tuffs) but they also contain boulder conglomerates on the Skerries.

Good exposures, which occasionally show bedding but are

K

otherwise massive and jointed, are found on the cliffs on either side of Church Bay. In the northern region good inland exposures are present about two miles south-west of Cemaes Bay, near the main road to Valley. A quarry by the road (at 348914) shows the tuffs cut by a Palaeozoic dolerite dyke. The best exposures, however, are at Llanrhwydrys church, west of Cemlyn Bay. At the south-west end of this shore section, a transition from the New Harbour group is well seen, dipping gently eastwards. Further coastal exposures of the Skerries group extend from Porth Wen to Bull Bay, and are chiefly of interest for the magnificent thrust planes, inclined to the north, which are found in the western end of the section.

Gwna group

This group of very varied rock types is one of the most remarkable in the Mona Complex: rock-types include jaspers, phyllites, spilites, quartzites, limestone, green grits and tuffs.

The igneous and pyroclastic rocks appear to form a single volcanic suite. The spilites are best exposed among the sand dunes south-west of Newborough (though afforestation has made them difficult of access), and can be seen almost as well on Llanddwyn Island. Rounded or flattened green 'pillows', with red jasper between them, are almost as fresh as when formed (fig 59). Lava flows of this type represent submarine extrusions of basic lava. The molten magma forms globules, up to two feet across, which are chemically altered by reaction with sea water. The jasper (quartz stained with an iron ore called hematite) is a common occurrence with spilites, though limestone is sometimes present instead. Three other major tracts of volcanic rocks, with associated limestones, are present at Cerig-ceinwen (south-west of Llangefni), south of Pentraeth, and west of Beaumaris. Good pillow structures can be seen in a field (421737) 200yd west of Cerig-ceinwen church.

Limestones, as well as being found with the spilites, are also associated with other rocks, particularly in the region between Bull Bay and Cemaes Bay. The quartzites associated with this group are also well exposed in the Cemaes Bay area, particularly in the strip-like outcrops which underlie the Ordovician conglomerates on Dinas Gynfor and Graig Wen.

At many localities the rocks of the Gwna group are not evenly

Fig 59 Spilitic lavas of the Gwna group, among the sand dunes near Newborough (*after Greenly, 1919*)

bedded, but are broken up into a mass of lenticular blocks, encased in a matrix of schist. Both Greenly and Shackleton quote a length of two or three miles for the largest of these blocks, though the majority are not more than a few feet long. They also agree in attributing this *mélange* to tectonic forces, but differ as to the mechanism involved. Greenly attributed this *mélange* to the breaking up of the beds during the folding and metamorphism of the Mona Complex, but Shackleton prefers a sedimentary origin, due to the uplift and tilting of the sea floor at the time of deposition, which resulted in the breaking up and sliding down slope of the beds. A subaerial origin is suggested in the British Regional Geology handbook.

It is not possible to appreciate the largest blocks in the field (they appear as lenticular outcrops on the 1in map), but excellent exposures of finer-grain *mélange* can be seen on the headland west of Llanbadrig church. Here the blocks in the *mélange* are rather more rounded than elsewhere, and can be more easily visualised as of sedimentary origin. At Carmel Head there is also a section in which it is relatively easy to envisage a sedimentary origin for the *mélange*. Beds of breccia alternate with phyllite and ashy grit, and look not unlike the undoubted Ordovician sedimentary breccias a few hundred yards to the east. Farther west, a good section is seen north of Ynys-y-fydlyn. In south-western Anglesey the section on the coast between Aberffraw Bay and Malltraeth sands is described by Greenly as being the finest in Anglesey.

Fydlyn felsitic group
This group is only found on the cliffs around Ynys-y-fydlyn, south of Carmel Head, and runs for a short distance inland. The rocks are highly acid, massive and white weathering, in some places with harder nodules, in others with a gritty appearance. Shackleton suggests that they may have been subaerial acid volcanics of the ignimbrite type.

Highly metamorphic and igneous rocks
Apart from the rock-groups that can be put in a regular order, all of which show only a moderate degree of metamorphism, there are three other groups that are distinguished by their texture and mineralogical composition and which are taken, particularly by Shackleton, to represent successively higher degrees of metamorphism. These are (1) the Penymynydd Schists; (2) the Gneisses; and (3) the Coedana Granite.

Rocks of the first group are best studied along the shore between Porth Nobla and Aberffraw, though good exposures are also present on Mynydd Llwydiarth, and a variety characterised by the mineral glaucophane forms the hill beneath the Marquess of Anglesey's column at Llanfair P.G. The gneisses occur in three main areas: on the hill just south of Carmel Head, in a belt adjoining the Coedana Granite (in part overlain by Ordovician rocks) and in a small area round Holland Arms. The granite, with an associated hornfels. formed by the baking of the surrounding country rock, is exposed in the Deri inlier and in a belt from near Llanerchymedd to Rhosneigr. It is regarded as the ultimate stage in the metamorphism of the Mona Complex. melting to form a true magma, which must have then forced its way upwards into its present position. The best exposures are just north-west of Gwalchmai, where there are large quarries, as well as natural exposures. Here the intrusive contacts can be examined.

ORDOVICIAN AND SILURIAN

The Lower Palaeozoic rocks in Anglesey are principally sediments (only at Parys Mountain are there well developed contemporaneous igneous rocks) which differ considerably in rock type and succession from those on the mainland. A striking feature is that rocks of the Cambrian system are probably completely absent from Anglesey, in great contrast to the mainland where they are several thousand feet thick. Most observers believe that Cambrian sediments were deposited in Anglesey, but that this part of the geosyncline was uplifted to form a land mass in late Cambrian times, and that the soft sediments were stripped off before the Arenig transgression.

The subsequent geological history of the region during Ordovician and Silurian times is difficult to decipher, because (1) the rocks have been eroded away from areas where the underlying Mona Complex is now exposed; (2) they are concealed beneath the Upper Palaeozoic rocks when these are present; and (3) in many places where they would otherwise be exposed they are covered by boulder-clay.

Four principal rock-types can be recognised:

(1) grits, sandstones and conglomerates. These were deposited in shallow water, with a fauna of brachiopods and trilobites.

(2) shales. Looking very like the shales elsewhere in Wales, these are usually blue-grey in colour, very fine-grained, and occasionally with thin laminae of siltstone. Typically black graptolitic shales are not found, though some graptolites are present.

(3) gritty shales. This may be used as a term for a variety of rocks, varying from a shale with scattered flakes, pebbles and grains (often angular) of Mona Complex rocks, to massive breccia beds of these rocks, interbedded with shales. Some blocks in these breccias are very large indeed (two to six feet long), and cannot have been transported far.

(4) oolitic ironstones. These are found at a number of localities, and come from more than one stratigraphic horizon.

Five main areas of Lower Palaeozoic rocks occur, each separated by areas of Mona Complex: around Llangoed, within the Barw Fault complex, around Llangwyllog, the Principal area (from Rhosneigr to Carmel Head and the north-east coast), and the Gynfor outliers (on the north coast east of Cemaes Bay).

Succession

The thickness of the Lower Palaeozoic rocks cannot be measured accurately, but is of the order of several thousands of feet. It also varies within the island.

Silurian	{ graptolitic shales of Parys Mountain, resting on a volcanic suite of Ordovician age unconformity
Caradoc	{ conglomerates, breccias, grits, ironstones and shales unconformity probably corresponding to the Llandeilo series
Arenig-Llanvirn	{ gritty shales, conglomerates, breccias, shales and ironstones transgressive sandstones, grits and conglomerates unconformity

Structure

The areas of Lower Palaeozoic rocks form a number of synclinal structures, between anticlinal regions of Mona Complex rocks. The structures are not simple, as faults break up the folds: both strike-faults, which run parallel to the fold axes, and (generally later) cross-faults, which offset fold axes and earlier faults (fig 60). The major strike-faults separate Ordovician and Mona Complex rocks, and there is some evidence to show that they were active during Ordovician times, as well as later. Where an axial plane cleavage is present, it is generally inclined to the north-west, indicating that the folds are 'leaning' to the south-east.

The Carmel Head Thrust is the most striking fault in northern Anglesey, and runs in an arc across the island from Carmel Head to Porth Cnwgl, near Amlwch. Along this line Mona Complex rocks were pushed south over the Ordovician for a distance estimated by Greenly as between 12 and 20 miles, though it is likely to be much less.

The Ordovician structures do not show a complexity comparable to that of the Mona Complex ones, nor do the rocks

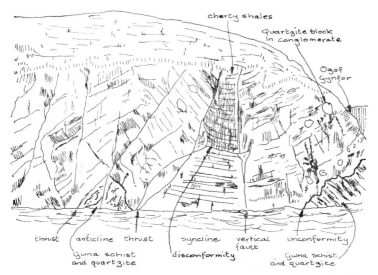

Fig 60   Folded and faulted Ordovician conglomerates, grits and shales, resting on the Mona Complex (*drawn from a boat*)

show any appreciable metamorphism. This is partly due to the fact that the compression and folding of the Caledonian orogeny was less severe, and also to a sheltering effect conferred by the Mona Complex. This acted as a rigid basement, rather like a series of paving stones, on top of which the lower Palaeozoic rocks behaved like a series of blankets under compression.

Basal Arenig grits and conglomerates

The basal beds are clean washed (with little clay matrix) sand-stones, grits and conglomerates, generally well bedded, and often flaggy, with a shallow water fauna of brachiopods and trilobites. Large-scale current bedding also suggests deposition in a shallow water environment with strong tidal currents. Most of the fos-sils are in fragments.

At Garth Ferry, opposite Bangor pier, whitish grits of this type are found on either side of the Gazelle Hotel. To the north-east, they are faulted against Gwna green schist. Exposures of these basal beds can be found along the Berw Fault and near Llangwyllog, but their best development is between Rhosneigr and Llanerchymedd (in the Principal area). At Llyn Maelog,

Rhosneigr, exposures occur along the north side of the lake, dipping to the north-west. Exposures are good around the hamlet of Carmel, where the grits form a low scarp, facing south-east over the Mona Complex. Fossils, particularly the brachiopod *Lenorthis proava*, may be collected from small quarries and natural exposures.

Lower Ordovician

The basal grits are overlain by three different rocks, which reflect different conditions in different parts of the island. In many places the grits grade rapidly upwards through fine sandstones to shales, representing a rapid decrease in the supply of coarse sediment, presumably due to deepening of the sea. This is the case over much of eastern Anglesey, as far west as Llanerchymedd.

Between Rhosneigr and Trefor, grits and conglomerates of rather different aspect succeed the basal grits, and may be about 3,000ft thick. They can most conveniently be seen in an old quarry at a bend in the B5109 road, 1½ miles east of Bodedern. The rock is a conglomerate, light green in colour, formed mainly of angular blocks of green schist, from the New Harbour group, with a matrix of finer fragments from the same source.

Farther north-east, the beds which succeed the basal grits are an intermediate group between the shales and the green schist conglomerates: blocks and pebbles of green schist occur but are scattered in a matrix of shale. These beds occur over a wide area between Trefor and Llanerchymedd; outcrops may be examined around Ceidio church, one mile north-west of Llanerchymedd, and in the ravine at Nantannog, one mile east of Llantrisant church.

These lower Ordovician beds include both divisions of the Llanvirn series, as 'tuning-fork' graptolites of both the *Didymograptus bifidus* and *murchisoni* zones are present. At no locality is the fauna very rich, and collecting is likely to prove unrewarding.

Upper Ordovician

The upper Ordovician is known in eastern Anglesey from graptolitic shales at Careg-onen, and also at Llangwyllog, while in the Principal area the region around Llanbabo affords the most rewarding exposures. A succession in the lower part of the Caradoc series can be pieced together from exposures at Llanbabo, and Fferam-uchaf, one mile to the west. At Fferam-uchaf, a dense black oolitic ironstone is found in old quarries just to the west of the farm overlain by dark graptolitic shales in the farmyard. At the church quarry, Llanbabo, shales with grits, probably overlying the graptolitic shales, contain brachiopods in the grits and graptolites in the shales. This occurrence of both types of fossils together is extremely useful, as it provides a means of correlating between shallow water rocks with shells, and deeper water shales with graptolites.

A different, but contemporaneous, series of rocks is found near Carmel Head. On Mynydd-y-garn and near Porth Padrig (on opposite sides of the Carmel Head Thrust) a remarkable series of breccia beds and shales rests unconformably on the Mona Complex. Massive breccias composed of blocks of Gwna green schist form the summit of Mynydd-y-garn, and pass up into finer breccia beds alternating with shale. In the exposures between Porth Padrig and Porth Newydd these breccias are very well exposed, and of undoubtedly sedimentary origin, since beds of breccia are interbedded with graptolitic shales (fig 61). The

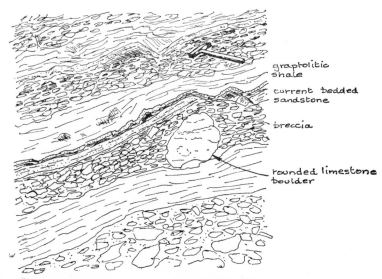

graptolitic shale

current bedded sandstone

breccia

rounded limestone boulder

Fig 61 Breccia beds and interbedded graptolitic shales at Porth Padrig, Mynachdy, near Carmel Head

breccia beds are remarkable, for not only are angular pieces of Mona Complex rocks included, but also blocks of an Ordovician limestone, which are very well rounded (boulders six feet in diameter are present). The fossils in these included limestone blocks—brachiopods and trilobites—are very little older than the graptolites in the shales.

These breccias may possibly be explained by supposing sedimentation to have been affected by tectonic activity. It is suggested that the Mona Complex blocks were broken off a fault scarp during fault activity, and then slid downslope to their position of deposition, together with the Ordovician limestone boulders. Breccias of this type are known from a number of localities in the Ordovician, close to the present outcrop of the Carmel Head Thrust: at Llanfflewyn, Gwaen-y-dog, north of Parys Mountain (in drill cores), south-east of Amlwch and near Point Lynas. It is tempting to link their occurrence to Ordovician faulting along this line.

Parys Mountain

At Parys Mountain is a unique occurrence of Ordovician volcanic rocks, Silurian graptolitic shales, and intensive mineralisation and silicification. The general structure of the mountain is very simple: the volcanic rocks are folded into a large isoclinal syncline, which closes at its west end and plunges eastward, with Ordovician shales 'outside', and stratigraphically beneath, and Silurian shales in the core, along the line of the great opencast pits. Thrust-faulting, and silicification (mineral replacement by silica) of all rock-types has obscured the junctions between the groups, so that it is not possible to determine whether the volcanic group is conformably related to either group of shales.

The volcanic rocks, all of a kind rather vaguely called felsites, are probably a suite of ignimbrites, perhaps with some rhyolites and ashes. Exposures of felsite are good along the south-east side of the mountain, and also along the north-west sides of the opencast pits. The best exposures of the contacts between the Ordovician shales and the felsites are along the scarp north of Trysglwyn.

The Silurian shales in the core of the syncline are only well exposed in the two great pits. Unsilicified shales are light grey and slaty, and silty laminae can be seen as stripes across the cleavage surfaces, together with small dark patches, which may represent animal burrows in cross-section. Silicified shales are a brighter blue in colour, very hard and flinty, and sometimes studded with pyrite crystals. There is no tendency to split along the cleavage planes, which seem to have become healed up. Graptolites, which can only be collected when the bedding and cleavage are parallel, can be found on the spoil, heap at the east end of the west pit.

The mineral assemblages found on Parys Mountain can be divided into three types :

(1) iron and copper pyrites within the silicified rocks, occurring as scatterings of minute crystals. These mineralised portions form broad ill-defined lodes.

(2) later mineralised veins, forming more definite fissures, infilled with quartz, rock fragments, iron pyrites, copper pyrites, galena and zinc blende.

(3) ill-defined ore bodies termed bluestone, a heavy granular rock dark bluish-grey in colour. Zinc blende and galena form the main constituents, but copper and iron pyrites are also present.

It is difficult now to find tolerable specimens of anything but iron pyrites, either on the spoil heaps or in out-crops, since the whole mountain has been so thoroughly worked over at the surface and many of the spoil heaps have also been reworked.

The oldest workings, which were first opened in 1798, were in the Silurian shales in the core of the syncline. At first the mines were worked by dozens of shallow shafts, on the site of the great opencast pits. Later these workings were opened out, and the pits were excavated. At this time the lodes north of the felsite had not been discovered, and activity began to wane at the beginning of the nineteenth century. In about 1830 the North Discovery Lode and others were found, and a second phase of prosperity, based on deep mining, lasted until 1890, when underground mining ceased. The deepest of these mines went down to 570ft below sea level. A third phase of activitiy has only recently stopped. Around the mountain are extensive shallow precipitation pits. Water from the flooded mines, charged with dissolved sulphates, was channelled into these pits and allowed to react with scrap iron dumped into them. Metallic copper was precipitated, while further treatment of the water yielded ferric oxide (ochre) which is used as a pigment. It is this which gives the prevalent rust colour of the tipheaps, the opencast pits, and the precipitation pans.

Recently several mining concerns have investigated both the old workings and the surrounding region, in a search for more ore. Since the lodes dip at a high angle to the north-west, they have drilled a series of inclined holes on the north slopes of the mountain, in an attempt to penetrate below the old workings, as well as along the strike of the lodes. Recent results are said to be encouraging, though any new development will depend largely on world mineral prices.

The north coast

The Ordovician rocks which are found on the north coast, between Cemaes Bay and Bull Bay, are folded and faulted into the Mona Complex, and are rather different from the Ordovician of the rest of Anglesey. Two grit and conglomerate divisions are overlain by cherty shales, and all were assigned by Greenly to the Upper Ordovician, on the basis of graptolites found in the cherty shales. Shelly faunas from the conglomerates have since proved to be of Arenig age, and as a result the junction between the conglomerates and shales must be taken as a disconformity —essentially an 'unconformity' but with no angular discordance, and representing a considerable non-sequence.

The lowest purple conglomerates are not present all along the section, but may be found at the old silica brick works at Porth Wen, and from there to the west side of Dinas Gynfor. They rest on quartzites of the Gwna group, and it is particularly instructive to trace the unconformity between the two units over Craig Wen, as irregularities in it suggest a coastal topography of the time, which was smothered under the conglomerate. The succeding pale conglomerates and grits are found everywhere along the section, and while at Dinas Gynfor they rest on the purple conglomerates, to the east and west they overlap them to rest directly on the Mona Complex. They owe their brown colour to siderite (an iron ore) in the matrix, and also have conspicuous white boulders of Gwna Quartzite. They are magnificently exposed (minus the purple conglomerate beneath) in the cliffs north of Ogof Gynfor, as is the marked unconformity separating them from the Gwna Quartzites beneath (fig 60). This succession, which requires some scrambling to reach, also has exposures of the disconformable contact between this conglomerate and the Upper Ordovician cherty shales. These latter rest on the conglomerate without transition beds, except that the top two feet of the conglomerate is formed from quartzite blocks in a matrix of shale, which contrasts sharply with the siderite matrix of the conglomerates beneath. Structurally, the section forms a microcosm of the folding and faulting of Anglesey as a whole. It is easy to visualise that such repeated folding and faulting will result in very complicated patterns of outcrop, which are very difficult to interpret when only partly exposed.

DEVONIAN AND CARBONIFEROUS

Carboniferous rocks are found in Anglesey and the adjacent mainland (Arvon) as faulted and tilted blocks, principally of Carboniferous Limestone; but other divisions of the Carboniferous system, the Millstone Grit and Coal Measures (including the barren red measures) are also present. Together, these form a microcosm of all the principal types of Carboniferous rock. The Devonian (Old Red Sandstone) rocks are found only in Anglesey and are of great interest, both because of their isolation from other areas of Old Red Sandstone, and because of their tectonic features.

Succession

Carboniferous	Coal Measures	Barren Red Measures
		Productive Coal Measures
	Millstone Grit	
	unconformity?	
	Carboniferous Limestone	
	unconformity	
Devonian	Traeth Lligwy Beds	
	Porth-y-Mor Beds	
	Traeth Bach Beds	
	Bodafon Beds	
	unconformity	

The Old Red Sandstone beds reach a maximum thickness of about 1,700ft in the Lligwy Bay region, and become thinner towards Llangefni. A total thickness of 3,800ft of Carboniferous rocks is present, but it is not all present at any one locality: the

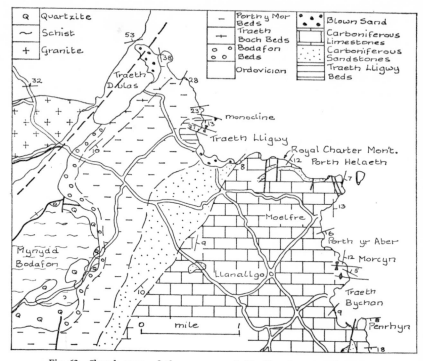

Fig 62   Sketch map of the area round Moelfre (*in part after Allen and Greenly*)

Millstone Grit near Bodorgan, and probably also beneath the Coal Measures under Malltraeth Marsh, rests not on the Carboniferous Limestone but on the Mona Complex.

Devonian

As shown in the reconstruction by J. R. L. Allen (fig 63), the area is thought to have been a large mountain-flanked valley, which was gradually silted up with debris brought in by a fairly large river system. To the west of Traeth Lligwy, the Gwna Quartzites of Mynydd Bodafon, which now stand up above both the Old Red Sandstone and Carboniferous rocks, were probably foothills on one side of the valley. Being much more resistant than the surrounding rocks, they now stand up, much as they did in Old Red Sandstone times.

The basal Bodafon beds are conglomerates and pebbly sand-

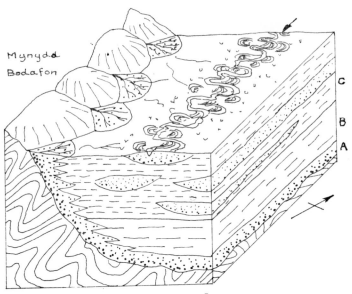

A Conglomerate facies : alluvial fans
B Calcareous facies : periodic drying out of lake
C Cyclical facies : river floodplain

Fig 63 Block diagram illustrating the conditions of sedimentation of
the Porth-y-mor beds (*after J. R. L. Allen, 1965*)

stones, representing alluvial fans and even screes, banked against
the slopes of the valley. The succeeding Traeth Bach beds are
siltstones and concretionary limestones. A rhythmic cycle can
be seen in both the Traeth Bach and the Porth-y mor beds, starting with coarse material which gives way to siltstone. Passing
up the cycle, the siltstones contain an increasing number of calcareous nodules, which may eventually coalesce to form a limestone. At the present day, such limestones are found in the soil
of a warm climate with a markedly seasonal rainfall. Lime in
the soil, in this case (Old Red Sandstone) silt laid down when the
valley was flooded, migrates upwards and forms the nodules.
The present-day deposit is called a caliche, while the conditions
of alternate flooding and drying out are termed playa conditions
(the floods are not thought to be seasonal).

The Porth-y-mor beds, which make up the bulk of the succession, consist of cycles of conglomerate-sandstone-siltstone-

marl, in general without limestones. They were probably laid
down by the river system. The topmost Traeth Lligwy beds are
of fine red sandstones and siltstones, laid down in a semi-per-
manent lake.

Fossils have not been found in these beds. Indeed, they are
rare in the Old Red Sandstone (fish and fresh-water crustacea
are found in the Welsh borders and in Scotland) as there was
little land flora to support animal life, especially in areas which
may have been subject to seasonal drought. The only indications
of life so far found are in the Traeth Lligwy beds. Many of the
bedding planes seem to have been churned up and disturbed by
animals which burrowed through the sediment in search of food.
No trace of the animals has yet been found, and it may be that
they were either soft-bodied, or that conditions at the time were
not favourable to the preservation of skeletal remains.

The Old Red Sandstone beds are folded, on axes which run
just south of east, with a complexity which recalls that of the
Lower Palaeozoic. Folding is acute at the south end of the coastal
outcrop on the north side of Lligwy Bay: here a rough axial
planar cleavage is developed, and some of the beds are overturned. Farther north, the axial plane cleavage is itself seen to
be bent, showing that the fold movements took place in at least
two phases, the first forming the axial plane cleavage and the
tight folds, the second producing a superimposed bending of the
whole. Small faults are present which are later than both periods
of folding.

Carboniferous Limestone
This, the lowest division of the Carboniferous system found in
Anglesey and Arvon, comprises mainly massive and laminated
limestones, but with some sandstones and conglomerates, dolo-
mites and cherts. Of the three areas, the Straitside area is poorly
exposed, and attention is better concentrated on the Penmon
area and the large area between Llangefni, Lligwy and Pentraeth.
The limestones and sandstones form distinctive country both
inland and on the coast. The low dip of the beds gives rise to
gentle dip slopes, ending in north-west-facing scarps, often
thickly wooded. Faults such as the Dinas Faults can be traced
by the displacement of the scarps. Much of the coast of these
two regions is formed by cliffs of nearly horizontal limestone;

though the cliffs are often vertical they seldom exceed 100ft in height, and can be easily studied from the wave-cut platform (tides permitting). At many places the cliffs have been quarried back, and the present cliff profile is not a natural one. It is often difficult to recognise this: the only clue may be the old blast holes along the edges of joints. Most of the stone so quarried was taken by boats, which anchored offshore, to form docks and asociated buildings in Liverpool and elsewhere. For this purpose the massive limestones were ideal, as they split horizontally along the bedding planes and vertically along joints, and required a minimum of dressing.

The lowest Carboniferous beds are not exposed on the coast, but can be examined in a quarry alongside the main A 5025 road near Lligwy Bay (at 489860), and in a recent road cutting nearby. Whitish sandstones and grits dip to the south-east: carbonised plant fragments are conspicuous and slickensided surfaces indicate fault movements. To the south the sandstones are only poorly exposed to Llangefni, but give rise to heath country which is, at best, suitable only for rough grazing. The lowest limestones form a scarp above them. At Llangefni an inlier of Mona Complex quartzite projects through and into the limestones. Greenly estimated that it must have formed a crag 100ft high in the Carboniferous sea, before being submerged in the sediments. It again forms a hill (Craig Fawr 456757) crowned by a disused windmill.

At the south-east end of Traeth Lligwy are found the lowest of the Carboniferous Limestones, here resting on a spectacular conglomerate, the Lligwy Bay Conglomerate. Between Careg-ddafad and the corner of the bay this conglomerate contains large blocks of Carboniferous Limestone, as well as blocks which can be matched with grits in the Ordovician rocks, and altered blocks of Parys Mountain rocks. The largest block of limestone is 11 x 5yd in plan, and stands up to 4ft above the beach and surrounding conglomerate; bedding in it can be seen to be horizontal. It is possible that this block is in fact a sea stack of Carboniferous times, surrounded by a pebble and boulder beach, which is now cemented round it. It is instructive to compare this mantling conglomerate with the modern beach: the loose blocks, pebbles and sand of the modern beach look at a distance indistinguishable from the Carboniferous conglomer-

L

ate. It is only when they are found to be loose that they can be distinguished.

To the east of the stack the section is difficult to interpret, and may be faulted in part. On the south wall of the bay is the formation called the 'Lligwy Bay Disturbance' by Greenly (fig 64).

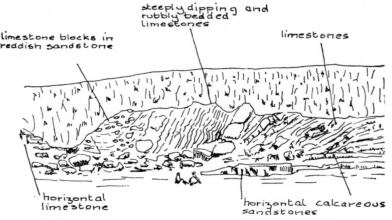

Fig 64   The 'Lligwy Bay Disturbance' on the eastern side of Lligwy Bay

Steeply dipping and very rubbly, partially broken-up beds of limestone are exposed in the cliff, and to their left have reddish sandy beds, containing blocks of limestone, banked against them. It is possible that the whole deposit was formed in a cave within the limestones, and has now been exposed by the cutting back of the sea cliff. Between Traeth Lligwy and Moelfre the succession is reasonably clear, and about 500ft of strata are exposed. West of Porth Helaeth 20ft of sandstones rest on a massive limestone (the Royal Charter Limestone) which is underlain by alternating limestones and shales. The Royal Charter Limestone was named after the sailing clipper which was wrecked on the reefs of the limestone in 1859. A recent book on the wreck refers to these cliffs as being formed of granite, no doubt poetic and commercial licence on the part of the author.

Between Moelfre and Red Wharf Bay, and also around Penmon limestones form the bulk of the cliffs, but sandstones and shales are found at a number of levels. Evidence of contemporaneous erosion of the beds is common, and can be studied best in the cliffs between Penrhyn Point and Huslan. Sandstones

and conglomerates pass abruptly into limestones, and local unconformities can be recognised: it is evident that erosion and
deposition alternated during these times.

Sandstone pipes are a peculiar feature of this coast, and can
be seen north of Moelfre (516868), at Porth-yr-aber (513858), at
Trwyn Dwlban (532820) and in the Huslan cliff (523833). The
pipes are approximately cylindrical bodies of sand, from a few
inches to several feet in diameter, and up to 12ft in height, occupying holes within the limestone (fig 65). In the case of those at

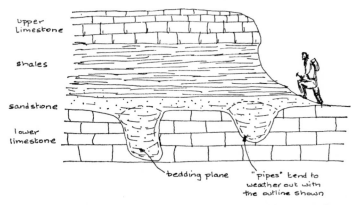

Fig 65   Cross-section through the sandstone pipes at Trwyn Dwlban,
near Benllech

Porth-yr-aber and Trwyn Dwlban the sandstone which infills
them is continuous with a bed of sandstone immediately above
them, but in other localities this horizon is marked only by a
prominent bedding plane within the limestones. Before infilling
by the sand, the pipes had the appearance of potholes on a limestone surface. Indeed, this is what they probably were: potholes
drilled into the limestone surface during a period of non-deposi-
tion. Similar potholes can be seen forming on some of the limestone shore platforms today, and are being drilled out by pebbles
moved by breaking waves. One locality where this can be seen
is on the north side of Porth-yr-aber, where a bedding plane dips
gently south, and is irregularly potholed.

A dolerite dyke is exposed in the cliffs at the south end of
Traeth Bychan, just west of a small cove (517846). Only about
18in thick, it follows a vertical joint in the upper part of the

cliff face, but veers away from it farther down. Little baking of the limestone has taken place.

On the Caernarvonshire mainland, the Carboniferous limestones are not well exposed, and their presence is not obvious Along the Straitside shore, from near Bangor to just beyond the Britannia Bridge, the lowest beds of the limestones and the underlying basal beds are reasonably well exposed. Soft red-stained Ordovician shales are present between the bridges at 550713, and these are overlain by 40ft of loam and breccia. The characters of these rocks suggest soil and scree: blocks of schist and shale are angular, and do not lie parallel to the bedding, while the loam is unlaminated, occasional blocks in it may stand vertically, and it passes up into shales containing land plants. Overlying the loam and breccia are conglomerates and sandstones, which form beach deposits, sometimes cutting into the loams. About 100ft thick, they are followed by cherts and limestones in a sequence very similar to that in Anglesey.

These lower Carboniferous rocks of the mainland were described by Greenly in 1928, with the fossil content named by experts.

Fossils occur in abundance throughout the Lower Carboniferous, but are difficult to extract from the massive limestones. Large productid brachiopods are common throughout, but are best seen in undercut ledges, where they weather proud of the rock. Corals, both solitary and compound, are found crowded in layers, or as colonies preserved *in situ* on bedding planes as mound-like masses. It is easiest to collect specimens from the dark shales, where they weather out and can be sifted from the debris adjoining these bands. Small brachiopods, crinoid ossicles, and coral fragments may be found.

It should be noted that the oldest Carboniferous Limestones of Anglesey are equivalent in age only to the youngest of the divisions (the *Dibunophyllum* zone) of the Carboniferous Limestones as found in the Pennines, South Wales and the Mendips. These areas were flooded by the sea at the beginning of Carboniferous times, but north Wales remained a land mass until much later.

Millstone Grit and Coal Measures
These beds are found mainly to the north-west of the Berw Fault,

principally beneath Malltraeth marsh, where thick alluvium con-
ceals most of the outcrop, though the Barren Red Measures are
also exposed on both sides of the Menai Straits near Caernarvon.
Only the Millstone Grit is at all well exposed, along the shore
near Bodorgan.

The Millstone Grit comprises mainly coarse rusty and gritty
sandstones with some shales. These shales contain the goniatite
Gastrioceras listeri, which dates the formation as being of lower
Coal Measures age—somewhat younger than the well-known
Millstone Grit of the Pennines. On the shore to the south-east
and east of Bodorgan House the grits rest unconformably on
Gwna schist. The schist forms an irregular surface, and it is not
difficult to compare this with present-day coastlines, with low,
sometimes undercut, cliffs.

Surface evidence of the Coal Measures is confined to over-
grown spoil heaps and an old chimney, marking a former col-
liery to the south-west of the A5 road, where it crosses Malltraeth marsh. The mines were known in medieval times, but
were not worked between 1640 and 1810, when working was
resumed until 1875. About thirteen seams of coal were known,
none of good quality, while geological conditions—the seams
dipping beneath the waterlogged marsh—made the mines very
wet.

The Red Measures are exposed at Foel Ferry, opposite Caernarvon, and at the disused brickworks at Griffiths Crossing
on the mainland. Red marls and thin pebbly sandstones form
rocks which are strikingly different from the Coal Measures,
and which represent a change from the stagnant coal forest
swamps to more arid conditions, with seasonal (?) rainfall, in
which the iron in the sediment is in an oxidised (ferric) state
in contrast to the reduced (ferrous) state of the iron in the Coal
Measures. North-east of Griffiths Crossing, at Dinas Head and
near Llanfair-is-gaer, the Red Measures and the Lower Carboniferous are strongly folded, thrust, and even overturned.

Sources

The monumental Memoir, written by Greenly in 1919, is an
indispensable source book for all aspects of the geology and
geomorphology of Anglesey. Shackleton's account of the Mona
Complex, in 1969, is essentially a re-interpretation of Greenly's

mapping, in the light of modern techniques. The present writer has recently published accounts of the palaeontology and stratigraphy of the Ordovician rocks, in 1969 and 1972 respectively, and also contributed short accounts of the Parys Mountain and Lligwy Bay regions in 1966 and 1969. J. R. L. Allen's careful study of the Old Red Sandstone appeared in 1965, and contains detailed sections of the coastal outcrops. Greenly, who on completion of his Anglesey Memoir turned his attention to the mainland of Caernarvonshire, published on the Carboniferous Limestones of Arvon in 1928, and on the Red Measures in 1938.

Chapter 13

Fossils

We have already referred to fossils and, in fact, defined them; but we were concerned with them only in so far as the different kinds served to identify the stratigraphical position of the rocks in which they occurred. We should in any case have had to discriminate between all these different kinds and given them names or numbers; but from the purely stratigraphical point of view they are simply useful objects preserved in the rocks.

When we realise that they are the remains of animals and plants that lived at the time the rocks containing them were laid down, they take on an altogether separate importance. Their study becomes essentially a part of the major science of biology —the science of palaeontology. Fossils are classified and named in the same way as are animals and plants living today. The full name is made up of two words, the genus followed by the particular species.

The fact that fossils have already enabled the geological record of the rocks to be put in chronological order has at the same time enabled the fossil record to be put in order. We can thus study the succession of different forms of animals and plants in so far as the parts of the individuals were sufficiently hard and resistant to be preserved.

The fossils with which we are concerned are the remains of organisms that lived in the region of what is now North Wales during the time covered by the rocks now present and exposed; that is, during the Palaeozoic era. We know, of course from other regions, the life of the Mesozoic and Cainozoic eras, so that whatever the geography of our region may have been then life would have flourished according to the time and the local conditions.

We look to the present in our attempts to reconstruct the

past, and it is obvious that different forms of life inhabit different environments. Thus, even within the restricted general environment where sediments are being deposited in the sea, we should expect sandy, limey, and muddy areas to support correspondingly different forms of life. Sandstones, limestones, and mudstones, all of the same age, will contain, as fossils, different 'excerpts' from the general life of that age. In the region of what is now North Wales during the Lower Palaeozoic era there does not seem to have been any great contrast between the biological conditions of the sandier and the muddier areas of deposition. Trilobites occur in rocks of varying lithological types, and so do brachiopods; but of the latter those that occur in the mudstones are specially mud-loving forms, as seen in their allies of today. The graptolites are confined to the mudstones. Limestones are rare among the Lower Palaeozoic rocks of our region; but corals are characteristic of that kind of rock, as is seen in the Carboniferous Limestone.

The question of fossil evidence in support of the principle of a continuous evolution of life throughout the course of time is beyond our scope. Such a principle is in any case the only reasonable one, and we may say that palaeontology not only supports it but proves it. But it is curiously reluctant to supply detailed evidence of the gradual transition from one form of life into another.

As most of our region is occupied by rocks of the Lower Palaeozoic era it is the fossils of this era with which we are chiefly concerned. Fossils are widely distributed in these rocks in our region but are by no means common everywhere, either stratigraphically or geographically. They are thus all the more important when found. In the lower part of the Cambrian they are, indeed, extremely rare. This does not necessarily mean that life was correspondingly meagre in its manifestation during that early time. Not so far away, in south Shropshire, the Lower and Middle Cambrian rocks are abundantly fossiliferous. though extremely poorly exposed compared with our magnificent displays in the Harlech Dome, for instance.

What are these 'forms of life' to which we are referring? Three groups are overwhelmingly the most common in the Lower Palaeozoic rocks and in every way the most interesting : the trilobites (*Trilobita*), a group of extinct arthropods; the graptolites (*Graptolithina*), an extinct group of uncertain biological affinites; and the brachiopods (*Brachiopoda*), a group of shelled animals living today but more abundant in past geological ages.

It must be understood that, naturally, rocks laid down as sediments in the sea will contain fossils only of those forms of life that lived where that was happening. It seems likely, how-ever—very fortunately—that it was just in those environments of shallow, or moderately shallow, water that life was most abundant.

The most surprising fact about the whole history of life as revealed by fossils is that when it is traced downwards through the ages it comes to a 'loose end' in those lowest, earliest, rocks that we call the Lower Cambrian. That is to say that, dominant among the earliest fossils, are the trilobites, members of that most advanced invertebrate group, the Arthropoda, and them-selves highly elaborate creatures. Evolution had evidently got well under way by the time we have any definite fossil record of it.

Lower Cambrian fossils in Wales are extremely rare, but we have the two notable trilobite finds, already mentioned, in our region : *Protolenus* (or an allied genus) in the Hell's Mouth Grits of St Tudwal's Peninsula, and *Pseudatops* in the Llanberis Slates.

As regards the Carboniferous rocks the chief fossils in the Car-boniferous Limestone are the brachiopods and corals, and in the Coal Measures bivalved molluscs (lamellibramchs), some of which probably lived in fresh water, the goniatites, an extinct group of coiled molluscs, and certain groups of plants.

Individual fossil specimens are nearly always imperfect, but by piecing together what is shown by a number of specimens we can make a reliable 'reconstruction' of the whole fossilisable part of the organism.

Most of the species of fossils whose names appear in our accounts are to be found among those illustrated in that most useful handbook, *British Palaeozoic Fossils*, issued by the British Museum (one of a series of three). There are also drawings of fossils in the Regional Geology handbooks on *North Wales* and *South Wales* (Institute of Geological Sciences). Practically every species of British graptolite is drawn and described in the Palaeontographical Society's *Monograph of British Graptolites* (Elles and Wood).

CHAPTER 14

Geology and Man in North Wales

It was the Carboniferous Limestone rocks of Flintshire which provided the earliest dwellers in North Wales with their first homes. The caves at Cae Gwyn and Pontnewydd near St Asaph have yielded finds which indicate that they were occupied by man in Aurignacian or Upper Palaeolithic times. One of the entrances to the Cae Gwyn caves has been silted up by glacial debris, beneath which was found an Aurignacian flint implement. This suggests that the ice returned to Flintshire after Aurignacian Man had lived in the Vale of Clwyd. At Pontnewydd the evidence is even more startling, as in this cave there have been found implements of felsite which look remarkably like Lower Palaeolithic hand-axes. If this is accepted then we have clear proof of Early Man in this Limestone country in inter-glacial times, in times when the climate was warm and semi-tropical. Modern workers are inclined to accept the evidence for very early settlement in these caves, as there is abundant evidence that Lower Palaeolithic Man lived at this period in similar caves in the Mid-Severn valley. This spread north-westward into North Wales is a strong probability.

The cave-dwellers lived for the most part near the mouths of the caves, and life must have been very hard for them, perhaps especially so in our area where they were at the very frontier of settlement, and where their food supply, represented by the animals of the chase, must have been limited; and where, in particular, supplies of flint suitable for the shaping of large implements such as the conventional hand-axe were severely limited. The quartzite and felsite used at Pontnewydd were in themselves very poor substitutes for flint. The early cave-dwellers in north-east Wales were, therefore, neither numerically strong nor culturally advanced.

Whatever we think of this earliest evidence of Man and his close association with the geological background, not only in providing him with a home but also with the raw material for hunting and for obtaining his essential food supplies, archaeologists are now agreed that even after the final retreat of the Pleistocene Ice Sheets, and when the severe cold of the glacial epochs was followed by the uniformly cold, dry climate with tundra vegetation, many of the Palaeolithic cave-dwellers continued to live on in the caves, and hunted such wild animals as the horse, the reindeer, and the mammoth. Their implements, it is true, became smaller in size though they were more carefully hafted into bone or wooden handles. Even so, this protracted Aurignacian culture—so characteristic of Britain and known generally as the Creswellian—was a poor substitute for the richer life of the great caves of Central France and Catalonia, where the richness of the chase is reflected in the wonderful rock paintings in the caves for which these limestone caves have no parallels either in Aurignacian or Creswellian times.

Slowly the climatic conditions improved with rising temperatures and increasing dampness as we enter the phase between the Old and the New Stone Age which is technically known as the Mesolithic. The flint implements became smaller and smaller, but the hafting was more delicate and expertly done. The archaeologists distinguish between the native and intrusive industries of this period. In north-east Wales Mesolithic folk still lived near the mouth of the Gop Cave, situated just a little to the north of those of Cae Gwyn and Pontnewydd. Here all the Mesolithic flints that have been found are classified as native industries, but as we approach the coast at Prestatyn, still clinging to the limestone cliffs, we find intrusive microlithic industries. These are known as Tardenoisian from the type site at Fère-en-Tardenois in northern France. At Prestatyn the implements themselves are worked from the local carboniferous chert, and very often from flint derived from pebbles on the sea-front. The latter have come from outside areas as a result of glacial movements in the Irish Sea and the sorting out of the glacial debris by marine action. The workmanship of the Prestatyn flints leaves no doubt whatsoever as to their cultural associations. The Mesolithic was the age of the food-gatherers, the fishermen, and the hunter of small game at the edges of the ever increasing forests. Nevertheless, the indebtedness of man, poor though he might be, to the geological endowment is unmistakable.

The Neolithic Age which followed was the Age of the First Farmers, when civilisation in the sense of the cultivation of crops and the domestication of animals, coupled with the art of pottery-making, entered our land. The present view is that the coming of the Neolithic colonists by land and sea routes from the Mediterranean shores was a gradual process. On their arrival in Britain they appear to have fused in many places with the survivors of the Mesolithic folk, especially in the uplands and on the coastal margins. The Neolithic people are known archaeologically not only from their dwelling sites and their pottery, but also from their arrow heads and stone axes (many of them carefully polished) and, possibly, above all, from their great burial chambers known collectively as the Megalithic Monuments. The main theme of this chapter is to show that geological considerations are all-important in relation to the various aspects of Neolithic civilisation listed above. No attempt will be made to discuss the archaeological problems involved—a simple reference to the type of rock employed is all that can be attempted. If we examine some Neolithic pottery, as, for example, that found at Pant-y-Saer in Anglesey, we note that the clay used was frequently tempered with crushed limestone. In this case it was locally obtained, but in many other cases the limestone must have been transported over considerable distances. This question of long-distance transport is, of course, an indication of primitive trade. Nowhere is primitive trade at this period better shown than in the case of the flint arrow heads. The distribution of flint arrow-heads in North Wales—a land sadly deficient in local supplies of flint—indicates, on the one hand, material derived from south-eastern sources (most likely the Wiltshire Downs), and, on the other, material derived from Antrim and north-eastern Ireland. The Irish arrow-heads are easily distinguished, being manufactured from Ochreous flint.

When we come to consider Neolithic stone axes and the Megalithic tombs themselves, we move into a more westerly location in North Wales. For the making of the new tools fine-grained, yet tough, igneous and metamorphic rocks were essential. Quite small exposures of suitable rock are known to have been exploited, and several axe factories came into existence. On the slopes of Penmaenmawr mountain the debris of a regular factory where axes were manufactured on a large scale from the local augite-granophyre has been found. The products of this famous factory seem to have been traded far and wide. Many axes are found in the immediate locality, others are known from places as far afield as Anglesey, the Severn Valley, Yorkshire, Glamorgan and even Wessex. A similar factory utilising a local outcrop of picrite at Hyssington in Montgomeryshire had an equally wide distribution of its products. In most cases, the axes were made from the loose scree blocks on the mountain slopes, but at one of the factories at least, at Mynydd Rhiw, near the tip of the Lleyn peninsula in Caernarvonshire, the rock is known to have been quarried directly from its outcrop—a narrow zone of schist produced by contact metamorphism of shale by intrusive dolerites. The method employed would seem to be similar to that of primitive open-cast mining.

The earliest Neolithic immigrants into North Wales seem to have entered the area very largely by sea. It was previously thought that the Megalithic Builders did not arrive in Northwestern Europe until towards the end of the third millennium BC, but now recent radio-carbon dating places their introduction into western Britain before the third millennium opens. The process of invasion seems to have gone on for many generations, and so the Neolithic Age gains considerably in length and importance. As the Age progressed it would appear that more and more colonists used the sea-routes. We are not certain why they came or, indeed, what they were looking for. It is obvious from the location of their tombs that they were looking for patches of fertile land whereon to practise the new arts of civilisation. Archaeologists have long pointed out that they were also in search of precious minerals among the ancient rocks of the western peninsulas of the continent. Mineral prospectors and merchant adventurers they undoubtedly were, but it is also clear that they must have been driven onwards by some powerful religious cult, the details of which are unknown to us, except that it must have had a close association with Cult of the Dead, for among the most spectacular features of the field archaeology of north-western Wales are unquestionably the remains of their massive collective burial chambers built for the most part of enormous upright stones set alongside one another above ground and covered by corbelled vaulting, the whole structure frequently buried beneath a massive cairn or earthen barrow, which has often been denuded away, leaving the great stones uncovered today. The enormous size of the stones employed in the building of these tombs fully justifies the adjective 'Megalithic' (great stone), now generally used by archaeologists to describe these most spectacular survivals of Neolithic culture.

Detailed examination of the stones employed in the erection of these tombs points to the fact that they were largely local in origin—grits, conglomerates, and coarse sandstones. This is certainly the case with the large tombs in Anglesey, and in the Conway valley, as well as those of Ardudwy that lie behind the Merioneth coast. It would appear, however, that when a suitable outcrop of limestone rock occurred, it was often used directly in the construction of a Megalithic grave. The Glyn monument in eastern Anglesey seems to have been constructed directly out of the local geology. An outcropping slab of limestone had been levered up and shifted sideways, so that it rested on a neighbouring slab, then the front and back of the major slab had been propped up, and filled with small uprights. Beneath the natural slab the actual grave was then excavated.

We cannot leave this important relationship between the geological endowment and human utilisation in Megalithic times without reference to other aspects of the Cult of the Dead, which seems to have formed the central theme of Megalithic religion. For example, at the famous Anglesey tomb of Bryn Celli Ddu, there is a whole scatter of broken white quartz stones near to evidences of cremated remains, suggesting that the white quartz stones possessed some special sanctity in association with the dead. It should not be forgotten that so great was the impact of the Megalithic cult in Western Europe that its memory died very slowly, and we still find the church and chapel cemeteries of North Wales containing numerous graves whose surface is covered with white quartz gravel—albeit now commercially produced.

In the Ages of Metal which followed, we find North Wales strewn with bronze weapons, spears, axes and celts, and later on with iron swords and metal shields. Objects of worked gold such as the gold lunulae, or breast-plates, frequently occur especially in relation to the transpeninsular traffic associated with the continued use of the seaways. Almost all this great range of metal objects is of Irish or continental origin, and there is at present no evidence that the metal resources of North Wales functioned in these developments. Native deposits of copper, as at Parys Mountain in Anglesey, and native gold as in the Mawddach valley, seem to have gone unworked until Roman times. It will be more convenient to deal with the development of these native metalliferous resources in the later centuries when they reach their fullest exploitation by man. We cannot, however, leave the prehistoric period without pointing out that the rocks of North Wales were often used for constructional and other purposes in the Age of Metal. One example drawn from the native Iron Age must suffice. The great hill-fort with the characteristic name of Bwrdd Arthur (Arthur's Table), sited on the top of a prominent flat-topped limestone hill behind Llanddona in Anglesey, is defended by a single stone rampart, as is characteristic of many of the hill-forts of north-west Wales. The rampart around Bwrdd Arthur is built of upright slabs of limestone arranged so as to form the sides of a trench eight feet wide —the intervening space being filled in with rubble. This system of wall-building is common in most limestone areas, and can be seen again at the Romano-British walled village of Din Lligwy, and, occasionally, in the much later field walls in the district.

The Romano-British period lived on after the Roman troops had departed, and it was in these centuries that Christianity first entered our western lands. There had been some Christianity in south-eastern Britain during the period of the Occupation, but with the Barbarian Invasions of western Europe Christian refugees escaped by the western seaways and arrived on our western seaboard. Their presence is well-documented archaeologically as they erected inscribed tombstones over the graves of the departed, and these are most thickly distributed in the north-western and south-western peninsulas of Wales, as may be expected from their use of the seaways. The early inscribed memorial stones were no more than simple stone slabs with a Latin, or sometime an Ogham, inscription or both, and possibly a roughly-cut cross or other Christian symbol. It has been noted that even the later memorials, which took the form of more elaborate richly decorated crosses in the late tenth and eleventh centuries, were forced to keep their ornamentation to bold clearly cut forms by the rough grain of the stone material available in north-west Wales. This is a countryside of hard granites and grits or else shales, slates or volcanic ashes.

In the early Middle Ages, Christians increasingly tended to bury their dead in church cemeteries, or even inside churches and monasteries, and the recumbent slab, most often with a well-cut effigy, replaced the isolated upright pillar-stone of the classical tradition. These later tombs have been studied in detail, and show an interesting chronological and geological sequence. Those found in north-west Wales before the conquest of 1282 were both few in number and generally rough copies of English models, but with the final settlement of North Wales in the last half of the thirteenth and the first half of the fourteenth century there was a sudden flowering of the stone craftsman's art as far as funeral slabs were concerned. The new gentry and petty chieftains lay buried inside their churches in massive tombs with recumbent effigies. Judging by the number of stone carvings of this period it would appear to be the fashionable practice of the day. The focus of interest also changed. No longer was north-west Wales the headquarters of the native princes. The more influential gentry moved eastwards and, incidentally, towards territories where the local gentry much favoured the stone craftsman's art. The ideal sandstones and limestones he mostly required lay along the Flintshire coast and in the hills overlooking the Cheshire Plain. Here were to be found the fine-grained sandstones on which delicate and detailed work could be done. The limestones of Anglesey and the north coast of Wales were certainly used, but on the whole, they were either too coarse or of a nature that flaked badly when split. So it was from the quarries of north Flintshire, in particular, that the best grained material was to be obtained. We know that it was shipped by sea along the North Wales coast and inland up the river Dee.

We can now turn from the sepulchres of the dead to the churches of the living. The earliest churches of the Celtic saints were never intended for congregational worship. They were just prayer-cells for the saint and his immediate followers. They were built of wattle and daub, and later replaced by timber structures. It was only if they had been well placed or were of special sanctity that they were then rebuilt in stone. We are interested in the stone that was used. The picture revealed is almost a replica of that indicated by the tombstones themselves. The churches of North Wales furnish a diversity of building stones, and show a considerable degree of variation consistent with the stones nearest to hand. In the western portion of North Wales the medieval builders became adept in the use of irregular material, and would seem to have utilised any stone, even glacial boulders, that came to hand. There was, however, everywhere a deficiency of durable building stone suitable for windows and ornamental work generally, and much of this material had to be brought from the Coal Measure sandstones of eastern Flintshire and Denbighshire, especially it would seem from the well-known quarries of the Point of Ayr where the Talacre stone was obtained. This comes from the basal beds of the Coal Measures, and is a homogeneous, fine-grained, compact sandstone eminently suitable for ecclesiastical work.

When we look at the eastern side of North Wales we see a difference in the building stone used for the older churches. Here, as is to be expected, Carboniferous Limestone seems to have been widely used, while we have already seen that the eastern side is well endowed with good sandstones as well. The Abbey of Basingwerk and St Winifred's chapel at Holywell have naturally relied greatly on the famous Talacre stone, while a comparison of the building stone used in St Asaph's Cathedral and in St Deiniol's Cathedral at Bangor brings out the east-west contrast particularly well. St Asaph's Cathedral shows at least four varieties of stone in the structure of the older part of the building. Most conspicuous of all is the Gwespyr Sandstone, the Talacre stone. Carboniferous Limestone is well represented by limestone of similar texture, but with a marked nodular structure—the rocks of both systems outcrop within a short distance of the cathedral. Finally, the red sandstone of the Triassic is represented, in spite of the fact that it is a soft crumbly rock not very well suited for weathering. In confirmation, as it were, we note that in modern renovations (with very much better transport conditions than were available in the Middle Ages), the Red Hollington stone of Staffordshire has been used—a stone that is much more resistant to weathering. In sharp contrast, at Bangor Cathedral in the west most of the work is of random

M

rubble masonry with grit-stone dressings—the only important exception being the sixteenth-century west tower which is built of sandstone ashlar partly red and buff.

We should next consider the great medieval castles of North Wales. While they are less numerous than the churches, they are, nevertheless, far more spectacular features of the landscape. It is convenient to consider the castles in two groups—the English and Welsh castles built before the conquest of 1282, and the Edwardian castles erected as part of the pacification of Gwynedd after the conquest. The first group are interesting in that we find that for the most part they were all built of local stone, and we get a sharp division between east and west in North Wales, dependent upon the general political and military situation. The English-built castles are found in the east, and the Welsh castles in the west. It is obvious, therefore, that the general geological contrasts between the two terrains are equally clearly reflected in the type of building stone used. Of the seven English castles, Prestatyn is built of local grey limestone with yellowish sandstone walls, although it is possible that the latter may be derived from the famous Talacre quarries at the Point of Ayr. The stone used at Dyserth is the local Carboniferous Limestone, while at Holt the local red sandstone is used. Soft red sandstone from local quarries seems to have been used at Ruthin giving the castle its characteristic reddish colour from which it derived its Welsh name of Castell Coch (Red Castle). Hawarden Castle is built of sandstone with an addition of quartz to give almost the appearance of a conglomerate; Caergwrle has the local Cefn y Fedw sandstone; while Denbigh Castle shows that Carboniferous Limestone was the main building material. This is an admirable stone of good weathering properties, and much used in medieval building. Some local red sandstone of Triassic age has helped with window and lancet frames.

The more westerly located Welsh castles that are known to have a pre-Edwardian history indicate an entirely different geological background as far as their building stone is concerned. Dolwyddelan shows large blocks of rhyolitic tuff and highly cleaved black shale. Dolbadarn has building blocks of purple and green slate associated with blocks of grit, and glacial boulders interspersed with masonry. Deganwy, another Caernarvonshire castle of pre-Edwardian date, is built largely of local rhyolite. The rhyolite forms blocks of irregular shape which are hard to dress. Great quantities of mortar appear in the castle walls in consequence. The well placed Castell Dinas Bran in Denbighshire is constructed of local mudstone. This rock is rather intractable for building purposes—a factor which probably accounts for the very rough character of the walls in this castle. Carnddochan Castle in Merioneth is built with local volcanic tuff, while Criccieth in Caernarvonshire has blocks of pink igneous rock, generally known as felsite, together with shale and many rounded boulders of glacial drift. We know that this castle was adopted by Edward I, and certain changes made in its defences. Edward possessed control of the sea, and could obtain building material from farther afield, and we note in consequence some coarse pebbly sandstone, almost certainly from the Carboniferous rocks of eastern Anglesey, used in the later rebuilding.

When we turn to examine the great castles built by Edward I, we must remember that his plan for controlling North Wales was a unified one. He erected a series of castles at intervals along the North Wales coast and relied largely on his command of the sea from his base at Chester to maintain communication between them. This use of sea transport made possible a wider range of choice of building material, and the masons were no longer hampered by the limitations of local sources of supply. Flint Castle and walled town, which was one of the first to be built, shows the use of a yellowish sandstone from the Coal Measures. In addition, a red sandstone containing small pebbles is used as ashlar in parts of the west wall of the castle, and in the Great Tower. This almost certainly came from the Middle Bunter Sandstone of the Wirral peninsula and the Chester district. Farther west, at Rhuddlan, the curtain walls and the revetment walls of the castle ditch are built mainly of grey Carboniferous Limestone. Coal Measure sandstone also appears together with large blocks of a distinctive purple sandstone in the lower courses of the towers. Triassic sandstone is used for window frames and other purposes. This stone was almost certainly carried by sea from the Chester area.

To the westward again is Conway Castle, probably the best preserved example of medieval military architecture in Britain. The walls of this great castle are built entirely of the hard

Silurian grit that forms the ridge on which the castle stands.
A red and white mottled sandstone is much used for window-
casings and mouldings in the King's and Queen's Towers. This
stone almost certainly came by sea from the Triassic rocks of
the Chester district. Next come two of the best known castles of
North Wales, Harlech and Caernarvon. The walls and towers
of the former are built of hard, grey Harlech grit derived locally
from the lower beds of the Cambrian system. Slabs of slate are
interspersed with grit masonry. At Harlech the door lintels and
window frames are worked in a soft yellowish sandstone, resembling very closely the Carboniferous sandstones of Anglesey.
The great pile of Caernarvon is known to most people throughout the land. Altogether four different types of building stone
were used in the construction of the castle. The principal stone
is a compact variety of Carboniferous Limestone, doubtless derived from Penmon in Anglesey. Next comes a light brown
Carboniferous Sandstone obtained from rocks outcropping along
the Menai Straits, while minor use is made of material derived
from Ordovician shales, and the sea-borne red sandstone from
the Triassic rocks around Chester. It is seemly to leave to the
last Beaumaris Castle in Anglesey, because this was the last of
the great Edwardian fortresses to be built after the Welsh rising
of 1294. The building material consists of three main elements:
first, and most important, Carboniferous Limestone, secondly a
pebbly sandstone used for doorway lintels, window casings and
the like, and finally some metamorphic rocks, including the Pre-
Cambrian green schists of Anglesey are seen among the
masonry. This very brief survey of the building stone used in
the North Wales castles is certainly warranted, not only because
the great castles stand out in the human landscape, but also because the range of geological material utilised by the builders
extends from the Pre-Cambrian, at one extreme, to the Triassic at
the other.

If we now take for granted the geological foundations of the
magnificent scenery of North Wales, capitalised by modern man
through the tourist industry, we can proceed to a discussion of
four remaining contributions made by the geological background to the economic life of the community in North Wales
in modern times. These should include copper and gold mining
in the north-west; the utilisation of geological endowments

which brought the industrial complex of the north-east coalfield into being, and helped to maintain it in times of economic stress; and above all, the geological factors which have made the slate industry of Caernarvonshire and Merioneth world-famous.

Copper has been mined in North Wales since Roman times, if not since prehistoric days. Hammer querns found at the famous Parys Mountain mines, two miles from Amlwch in north-eastern Anglesey, are thought by archaeologists to belong to the Celtic period, contemporary with the Roman occupation, and to have survived in use for long afterwards, although they have not yet been found in association with dateable objects. There is no evidence, of course, that the Romans worked these mines at the Parys Mountain or on the Great Orme in Caernarvonshire themselves—all the evidence we possess indicates that the mines were worked by the natives, and the ore either bought or commandeered by the invaders. It was in the late eighteenth and early nineteenth centuries that the Parys Mountain mines reached their hey-day when about 1,200 men, women and children were employed in the copper industry at Amlwch. After being mined on the mountain the ore was initially smelted at Amlwch and then transported by sea either to South Wales or the Deeside for further treatment. The significant feature was that during this period Anglesey copper from the Parys Mountain completely dominated the entire European market, largely due to the influence of Thomas Williams (1737-1802), an Anglesey man who was universally known as the Copper King.

In the next century the Parys Mountain mines came under the influence of Cornish 'captains', as they were called. These men were able to apply their experience in the Cornish tin mines, and introduce deeper mining methods. They were, however, soon faced with foreign competition and a fall in the quantity and quality of the Anglesey ore, so the fortunes of the Parys Mountain declined in the second half of the nineteenth century. Apart from the outstanding importance of the Parys Mountain (and to a far lesser extent of the workings on the Great Orme), sporadic mining of copper took place near Llanberis and at Drws-y-Coed in the Nantlle valley. Mining in this area can hardly be described as an industrial undertaking. It is better described as a rural industry operated by part-time farmers.

A traditional glamour always surrounds gold. This precious

mineral occurs sporadically in the North Wales rocks more particularly associated with the lodes that lie in the Menevian and Lingula beds of the Lower Cambrian on the hills above the estuary of the Mawddach in western Merioneth. Gold is said to have been worked in Roman times, and there are persistent reports of gold being washed out of river alluvium in this area. Many of the more important lodes in the Mawddach area, such as the Vigra, Clogau, Cwm Eisen, and Dol-y-ffrwnog, were originally worked for copper. It was the discovery in the mid-nineteenth century of the nearby St David's lode that proved to be the most valuable commercially. It is worthy of note in a human context that it is the mines in the lower part of the Mawddach valley that have provided the gold for numerous royal wedding rings, including those of Queen Mary, the Princess Royal, Queen Elizabeth the Queen Mother, and Queen Elizabeth II.

We have already seen that the limestones of Anglesey, especially those quarried near Penmon and Benllech, were extensively used in building the great castles of Caernarvon and Beaumaris at the end of the thirteenth century. In the early nineteenth century, this same Penmon stone was used for the construction of the two Menai bridges, Conway Bridge and Penrhyn Castle. At the same time, building stone from the Moelfre quarries in north Anglesey was used to build the North Stack Lighthouse, Holyhead Harbour and even Birmingham Town Hall. We must remember also that the igneous rocks of Caernarvonshire are very suitable for use as road stone, and the largest 'granite' quarry in the country, at Penmaenmawr, has an output of three-quarters of a million tons a year. This 'granite' is used for road surfacing and as a concrete aggregate, and much of the material is exported by sea to Merseyside, South Wales and even the Thames valley. Granite from the Trevor quarries in the Lleyn Peninsula is extensively used as a building stone and for monumental work. The present output of hardstone from this area is well over a million tons a year, of which about forty per cent is used for road work. The granite found at Trevor is particularly suitable for shaping into small rectangular blocks known as 'setts', considerably in demand for road construction in large towns and cities.

We can now turn our attention to the industrial area of north-east Wales. It rests on a series of rock outcrops trending in general from north to south. The systems concerned are the Ordovician, Silurian, Carboniferous and Trias—a comparatively small but extremely important part of the whole stratigraphical sequence. These rocks contain a wide range of useful commodities for modern man. The folding at the close of Silurian times was responsible for the formation of slate in the older Palaeozoic strata. Quarries have been opened in these rocks wherever the slate proved to be of marketable value. The Carboniferous Limestone is of considerable economic importance. In the north-west corner of the area, there are very pure limestones which are greatly in demand in modern chemical industries. Much of this limestone is also especially suited for cement-making. The sandstones in the middle of the Carboniferous system are used for moulding sand in the steel works, and for making filter beds in water works. Some of the purest sandstones are used in the glass industry, and for making refractory bricks for lining furnaces; while some of the very fine-grained varieties are used in the preparation of abrasive soaps. Local silica in the sandstone series is used in making china and earthenware goods.

The upper part of the Carboniferous Limestone, the Millstone Grit, and the lowest part of the Coal Measures carry the metalliferous mines yielding both lead and zinc. The Coal Measures themselves yield both steam and house coal, gas and coking coal and, in addition, a variety known as cannel coal, found around Leeswood, Hope and Mold. Oil was at one time produced from this coal, and even later on when the oil industry was overtaken by the exploitation of natural oils in the USA and elsewhere these cannel coal works remained as the nucleus of an important chemical industry now located in the northern parts of Flintshire. Coal is by no means the only useful commodity present in the Coal Measures. There are the Coal Measures Iron ore, now largely disused, but formerly very important; marls for making terra-cotta, bricks, and fire clays—the latter used for making fire-resisting bricks for metallurgical furnaces. In contrast the mineralogical resources of the Trias rocks are not great, and the country occupied by them is given over largely to agricultural pursuits.   ,

We note, therefore, that in north-east Wales there exists in close association with the production of coal a great variety of geological materials that can be used in modern manufacturing processes, more particularly in the iron and steel industry, the chemical industries, and the manufacture of rayon and artificial textiles. It was this variety of inter-related industries that allowed the North Wales coalfield to withstand to a much greater degree than its southern counterpart (which had relied so greatly on coal extraction alone) the worst features of unemployment and economic depression that characterised the inter-war years. Surely, behind this picture lies a close relationship between rock type, rock content and human activity.

Turning to the slate industry, we reach possibly the most important of all geological associations with human life, and the one for which North Wales is best renowned. We know that the Romans used Welsh slate for paving and roofing purposes as early as the third century AD, but it was not until the nineteenth century, in particular, that the industry became organised on a vast commercial scale. Altogether, four areas in North Wales were involved in slate production during the century. There is no doubt that central Caernarvonshire was the most important producing area. Here the slates occur in beds of Cambrian Age and are mainly blue, grey or purple in colour. It is in this area that we find the important slate quarries of Penrhyn, Dinorwic and Nantlle. The Penrhyn quarries at Bethesda and the Dinorwic quarries at Llanberis claim to be the largest slate quarries in the world. They are of the open quarry type, the slates being obtained from a series of terraces and galleries sometimes 70ft high. The Nantlle quarries are deeper, due to the situation of the slate beds in a deep-sided valley. The second important region is in the neighbourhood of Blaenau-Ffestiniog. Here the slates are of Ordovician Age—mostly blue or grey in colour and of very high quality. In this region they are quarried in underground mines where the slate is reached by horizontal levels driven into the mountain side. In this way, huge chambers are created which may be as much as 120ft long, 40ft wide, and 100ft high. Slate-quarrying is also a feature of southern Merioneth, more particularly in the Abergynolwyn district where the quarries are located in Ordovician strata, and in the Corris-Aberllefenni district where the Silurian strata are worked. The rocks in this area are very hard, and as a result the production of slate slabs for billiard tables, brewery vats, and scientific benches is more important than the supply of roofing slates. The fourth region is in eastern Merioneth in the districts around Corwen and Llangollen. In this area, too, the slates are quarried from rocks of the upper part of the Silurian system. The slates are dark grey-blue in colour and are used for slabs, cisterns, and flags rather than for roofing slates. At the close of the nineteenth century North Wales was producing nearly half a million tons of slate annually, but in the present century, which saw the development of synthetic substitutes and the disturbance of sales following the two world wars, there has been a very rapid reduction in the output figure.

From the human point of view the slate industry produced a way of life almost of its own. The slate-quarrying settlements have a distinct character of their own—a dreary aspect, which results from the use of slate for building purposes—with houses, churches, chapels and schools all built of slate. Slate slabs form the boundary fences between household gardens as well as between fields, and likewise mark the resting places of the dead in every cemetery and burial ground. In attempting to understand the slate-quarryman's way of life we must not forget that the wave of industrial prosperity in the industry coincided with a period of religious awakening in Wales which followed in the wake of the Methodist revival in the eighteenth century. The overwhelming strength of Nonconformity was clearly associated with the industry, and the chapels in turn were instrumental in bringing about a very close integration of the religious, educational, artistic and political aspects of life. It was the chapels, with the schools, reading rooms, libraries and Eisteddfodau, that knit together a people who lacked an urban tradition. These institutions served also as valuable training grounds for future leaders in all branches of public life.

We cannot leave this aspect of the social background of the North Wales quarryman without mentioning one other 'institution' that literally grew up on the rock face itself. This was the quarryman's 'hut', or 'cabin' as it was called—the hut where all the workers went for their midday break and snack. These cabins were situated on each rock surface or underground floor of the slate workings. Apart from being huts for resting and eating, the cabins became the slate worker's 'parliament', where the problems of the day were argued and discussed. Each 'caban' had its president or chairman, who after the midday meal was ended called upon the secretary (usually a young recruit to the industry) to read announcements regarding forthcoming events. The chairman then asked for a topic for discussion. These topics were usually economic, religious, political or social, and might deal with trade unionism or current affairs. The discussions were of a very high order, and the last speaker (when the hooter sounded) was allowed to be the first speaker next day when the general discussion would be resumed. The slate-workers' cabans in this way assisted in creating men of character, integrity and ability, many of whom became local leaders in various spheres of social life. It should be remembered, too, that all this took place through the medium of the Welsh language, and it is in these parts of north-west Wales that the Welsh way of life, in consequence, has its deepest roots today.

While it is probably true to say that the quarry towns and villages are now living very largely on the moral, social and economic capital of the past, we must not overlook the fact that this capital was built up by men and women who lived not only 'very close to the soil', as is so often remarked, but in this case even closer to the very rocks themselves.

Glossary of Terms

ACID IGNEOUS ROCKS—Igneous rocks characterised by richness in the element silicon, together with the elements sodium and potassium.

AGGLOMERATE—Coarse volcanic pyroclastic material; ancient or modern.

ALLUVIUM—Sand and (especially) mud brought down by rivers in flood and deposited on the temporarily submerged land (the flood-plain or alluvial plain).

ANTICLINE—An upfold of a series of rocks.

ANTICLINORIUM—A compound anticline.

ARENACEOUS—Sandy. For sediments and sedimentary rocks.

ARGILLACEOUS—Clayey, muddy. For sediments and sedimentary rocks (wholly calcareous clays and muds usually excluded).

AUTOBRECCIATION—Internal disruption and fragmentation; applied to lavas.

AXIS of a fold—This has a variety of meanings and it is a useful term for the line, along the outcrop, about which the dip changes from one direction to the other. The 'axial plane' is a plane envisaged as bisecting a fold-structure.

BAND—A thin bed with a distinctive lithology, or fauna. (But the Black Band, an alternative name for the Dolgelley series, refers to a whole formation.) 'Banding', particularly 'ribbon banding', means thin bedding conspicuous in section, or such a structure as 'flow banding' in lavas.

BASIC IGNEOUS ROCKS—Igneous rocks relatively poor in the element silicon, and comparatively rich in the elements iron, magnesium, and calcium.

BED—A layer of rock. A thickness of a few inches or a few feet is usually implied. Hence 'bedding', bedding-surface'. 'bedding-plane'. 'Stratum' is synonymous.

BOULDER-CLAY—A stiff clay with pebbles and boulders of all sizes, these tending to be subangular in shape and often scratched. It is the most widespread and distinctive of the glacial deposits left behind on the melting of an ice sheet.

BRACHIOPODS (Brachiopoda)—One of the main groups of shelled invertebrate marine animals. The shell has two valves, unequal in size; the whole normally bilaterally symmetrical about a median line through the valves. Very common as fossils but not common today.

BRECCIA—A hard rock containing an abundance of relatively large angular fragments mixed with finer material.

CALCAREOUS—Composed of, or containing, calcium carbonate. For sediments and sedimentary rocks; also for skeletal material.

CHERT—Siliceous layers or concretions occurring chiefly in limestone formations.

CHLORITE—A greenish material, a silicate of iron, magnesium, and aluminium.

CIRQUE—A bowl-like hollow on a mountain side, with steep encircling cliffs. In the case for which the term is usually reserved it is formed by the erosive scooping action of ice.

CLEAVAGE—In geology, as distinct from mineralogy (where it refers to crystals), this always means 'slaty cleavage'.

COLUMNAR JOINTING—Polygonal jointing (in igneous rocks) result-ing in a columnar structure.

CONCRETION—A more or less spherical or ellipsoidal mass, a few inches or a foot or two across, consisting of material of different nature from that of the surrounding rock 'brought together' by some means, probably by percolating waters.

CONE-IN-CONE—A structure (sufficiently defined in the name) some-times present in concretions.

CONFORMABLE—A series of beds is 'conformable' when all the mem-bers lie regularly one on another.

CONGLOMERATE—A hard rock containing an abundance of pebbles.

CONSANGUINITY—Genetic relationship.

CORALS—Those members of the marine animal class Anthozoa that possess (calcareous) skeletons.

CORRELATION—The time-relation between strata in two or more re-gions. Strata are said to be 'correlated' when their time-equivalence is established.

COUNTRY ROCK—The rock invaded by an igneous intrusion or trav-ersed by a mineral vein.

CURLED BEDDING—Small-scale folded and contorted bedding.

DENUDATION—The stripping of rocks from a region by the removal of eroded material.

DEXTRAL FAULT. See *Tear fault*.

DIACHRONOUS—Not occurring, or produced, at the same time; not representing the same period of time.

DIFFERENTIAL EROSION—The unequal reaction to a uniform pro-cess of erosion whereby the more resistant rocks stand out among the less resistant.

DIP—The inclination of a rock-body or structural rock-surface, particu-larly of a bed or bedding-surface. The direction of dip is the direction of greatest slope, and the amount is the vertical angle with the horizontal.

DIP-FAULT—A fault aligned in the direction of the dip of the beds it affects.

DIP-SLIP—In faulting, the component of movement along the dip of the fault.

DIP-SLOPE—A slope of the ground determined by the dip of the beds.

DISCONFORMITY—An interruption in sedimentation, within a struc-turally conformable series of beds, representing a considerable 'non-sequence'.

DOLERITE—The commonest basic hypabyssal rock. Petrographically the coarser dolerites grade into the gabbros.

DOLOMITE—A white mineral, the double carbonate of calcium and magnesium, $CaCo_3 . MgCO_3$. The name is also used for the rock composed wholly or mainly of this mineral.

DOME—In geology a dome structure is one where the strata dip away from a central point.

DOWNTHROW—Refers to faulting. There are several slightly different meanings, but the 'downthrow side' of a fault usually implies the side on which there has been relative downward movement. 'Upthrow' (for the other side) is seldom used or required; 'throw' by itself always means 'downthrow'.

DRIFT—Deposits laid down directly from ice or from temporary lakes and streams connected with the ice. 'Glacial drift' is more explicit. Sometimes includes (particularly in a 'drift map') all superficial deposits other than local soil.

DYKE—An igneous intrusive sheet which cuts across the structure of the rocks into which it is intruded. Typically more or less 'wall-like'.

EARTH'S CRUST—The outermost shell of the earth. In thickness, of the order of 1/200 of the earth's radius.

EROSION—The general wearing away of rocks by weathering and the friction of material transported by water, ice, or wind.

ESCARPMENT—Usually means a ridge formed by a resistant sheet of rock, with an abrupt 'scarp slope' on one side and a 'dip slope' on the other.

EXPOSURE—A geological exposure is a place where a rock is exposed to view, naturally or artificially, not being hidden by vegetation, buildings, etc.

FACIES—A particular lithological, usually together with a particular faunal, character of a general stratal unit. The term comes into use chiefly when two or more contemporaneous units are being contrasted. We speak, for example, of a 'sandstone facies', 'graptolitic facies', 'shallow-water facies', the 'Old Red Sandstone facies' of the Devonian system.

FALSE BEDDING—Applies to bedding where the planes within a bed are inclined more or less regularly to the separation planes between the beds. A better term is 'cross bedding'.

FAULT—A surface of fracture in a rock-body along which there has been permanent displacement.

FAULT-BRECCIA—Crushed and broken rock along the plane of a fault or within a shatter-belt.

FELSITE—A very fine-grained igneous rock composed predominantly of felspar, with quartz.

FELSPAR (Feldspar)—The most important family of the rock-forming minerals; silicates of aluminium and, variously, potassium, sodium, and calcium.

FLAGS—Sandstones which split along the bedding into slabs.

FOLD—A bend in stratified rocks resulting in a reversal of the direction of dip.

FOLIATION—See *Schist*.

FORMATION—A distinctive lithological rock-unit of considerable thickness.

FOSSIL—The remains, representation, impression, or trace, in the rocks, of parts of an animal or plant. Hence 'fossiliferous' for rocks containing fossils. Fossils are named as are living animals and plants, eg, there is the trilobite genus *Agnostus* of which one particular species is *Agnostus fissus*.

190 GEOLOGY EXPLAINED IN NORTH WALES

FOSSIL FAUNA—The animal-fossil content of a stratigraphical unit. (Similarly, 'fossil flora'.)

GABBRO—The most typical of the basic plutonic rocks.

GALENA—The heavy grey mineral with metallic lustre, lead sulphide (PbS).

GENUS (plural *Genera*)—In the naming of fossils, as of living animals and plants, the genus comprises those species that are sufficiently alike to warrant their being placed in one small distinctive group.

GEOLOGICAL CYCLE—The general cyclic sequence of major geological processes and conditions throughout a region of the earth's crust.

GEOLOGY—The science of the earth; its composition, structure, processes, and history.

GEOMORPHOLOGY—The science of the earth's surface features; their character, origin, and evolution.

GEOSYNCLINE—An elongated downwarp of the surface of the earth's crust; used (exclusively?) for such a downwarp beneath the sea, the floor subsiding deeply beneath accumulating sediments.

GLACIAL PERIOD—A period in earth history when glacial conditions were so much more extensive than they are today, or at least so differently placed, that they covered regions, and extended down to levels, now enjoying a temperate climate. Also called 'Ice age'.

GNEISS—A coarsely crystalline rock, rather like a banded granite. In most cases it seems to be a metamorphic, rather than a purely igneous, rock.

GONIATITES (Goniatitina)—An extinct group (Devonian and Carboniferous) of molluscs coiled in a chambered symmetrical spiral. (Forerunners of the Mesozoic ammonites.)

GRADED BEDDING—Bedding within one rhythmic sequence (the whole or a part of it) in which there is a gradual transition from coarse to fine or fine to coarse (usually the former).

GRANITE—The most typical, and by far the commonest, of the acid plutonic rocks.

GRANOPHYRE—A very fine-grained microgranite with the quartz and felspar intergrown.

GRAPTOLITES (Graptolithina)—A group of extinct animal organisms of uncertain affinity, Cambrian to Carboniferous, but chiefly Ordovician and Silurian. The skeleton comprises one or more thread-like branches, an inch or a few inches long, with rows of small cups or tubes along one or both sides giving minute saw-like edges.

GREYWACKE (Grauwacke)—A lithological term with no precise meaning. It sometimes denotes beds of a hard grey rock within a series, or a whole series of grey rocks containing finer and coarser members.

GREENSTONE—A rather old-fashioned term for basic igneous rocks; particularly for dolerites, which are often of a dark greenish colour.

GRIT—A wide and vague term often applied to the coarser beds in a stratigraphical formation of varying lithology.

HILL-TOP SURFACE—An imaginary surface touching the tops of the hills.

HORIZON—A stratigraphical horizon is a plane within the rocks everywhere representing one and the same time. 'Stratigraphical level' means the same thing.

HYPABYSSAL ROCKS—Igneous rocks, such as dykes and sills, formed at no great depth.

ICE AGE—See *Glacial period.*

IGNEOUS ROCKS—Rocks formed by the cooling and consequent solidification of a molten magma. They comprise the plutonic, hypabyssal, and volcanic (incluling sub-volcanic) rocks.

IGNIMBRITE—Rock resulting from a dense hot incandescent volcanic ash-flow (a *nuée ardente*). Chiefly in use for ancient rocks so formed.

IN SITU—A rock *in situ* means that, in an exposure, the visible rock is part of the rock-body outcropping there, not a detached piece moved from some distance away.

INLIER—The outcrop of a stratigraphically or structurally lower rock surrounded by upper rocks.

MUDSTONE—A hard rock resulting from the consolidation of a rock-substance (magma) that has forced its way among pre-existing rocks. By far the commonest intrusive rocks are igneous rocks.

JASPER—Opaque silica stained a reddish brown by iron.

JOINTING—The fracture, without displacement, along a few particular plane-directions within a rock-mass. In stratified rocks, these directions are usually at right angles to the bedding.

LACCOLITE—An igneous intrusion of essentially sill-like habit but in the form of a flattened dome. The overlying strata have themselves become domed by the force of the intruding magma.

LAMINATION—See *Shale.*

LATERALLY—In stratigraphy, this refers to any direction along the lie of the strata.

LAVA—Molten rock material (magma) poured out on the earth's surface in volcanic action, and the rock formed as a result of its solidification. Used for both modern and ancient rocks. The rock is usually partly glassy and partly crystalline.

LIMESTONE—A hard rock resulting from the consolidation of a deposit or accumulation of calcareous material.

LITHOLOGY—The general mineral composition and texture of a sedimentary rock. Thus 'argillaceous limestone', 'coarse sandstone', would be statements as to lithology.

MAGMA—Molten rock-material; within the earth's crust, or poured out on the earth's surface (lava); a melt-solution of mineral substances.

MASSIVE—As applied to sedimentary rocks, thickly or obscurely bedded.

MELANGE—A medley of rock fragments.

METAMORPHISM—Mineralogical and textural changes in a rock-mass brought about by pressure or heat (or both together). Hence 'metamorphic rock' and the verb 'metamorphose'.

MICA—A family of rock-forming minerals, silicates of aluminium and potassium, with magnesium and iron in the dark varieties. Occurs commonly in igneous, sedimentary, and metamorphic rocks.

MICROGRANITE—In a wide sense the term covers most of the acid hypabyssal rocks.

MINERALOGY—The science of minerals.

MOLLUSCS (Mollusca)—One of the main groups of (mostly shelled) invertebrate marine animals, and today by far the most important of such groups. Also very abundantly represented as fossils.

MONOCLINE—A structural unit, a pronounced bend, in otherwise nearly horizontal strata.

INSTRUSIVE ROCKS—Rocks formed by the solidification of a molten deposit of mud.

NAPPE—A recumbent fold.

NON-SEQUENCE—In a conformable series of beds, a gap in the rock-record, a depositional hiatus, representing a time during which no permanent deposition took place there. Non-sequences are often difficult to detect with certainty.

NUEE ARDENTE—See *Ignimbrite*.

OOLITE—A sedimentary rock, usually a limestone, sometimes an ironstone, composed of small rounded grains.

ORE—A mineral aggregate from which one or more valuable constituents may be extracted.

OROGENY—Mountain-building. Used with the implication that this results from compressive folding within the upper part of the earth's crust.

OUTCROP—The area, strip of ground, line. or place where a particular rock-body or rock-surface emerges at the earth's surface. The verb can be either 'to outcrop' or 'to crop out'.

OVERFLOW CHANNEL—A feature of drainage under glacial conditions; a channel or notch cut by the waters overflowing from a lake ponded back by ice.

OVERLAP—See *Unconformable*.

OVERSTEP—See *Unconformable*.

OVERTHRUST—See *Thrust fault*.

PALAEOGEOGRAPHY—Geography (physical) of past geological ages.

PALAEONTOLOGY—The science of the life of past geological ages, as revealed by fossils.

PARENT ROCK—A rock *in situ* from which detached, perhaps far-travelled, particles, pebbles, or boulders have been derived.

PERIOD—In addition to its ordinary general sense, it is used specially for the period corresponding to a stratigraphical system.

PETROCHEMICAL—Pertaining to the chemistry of the composition and formation of rocks.

PETROGRAPHY—See *Petrology*.

PETROLOGY—The science of rocks in themselves; particularly the study of their mineral composition and texture (their 'petrography') which can only be revealed, in any exactness and detail, in thin slices under the microscope. From these facts is inferred their manner of formation.

PHYLLITE—A compact schistose rock, the individual minerals not being well defined.

PILLOW-LAVA—A (basic) lava formed as a submarine flow and having a structure resembling a pile of pillows.

PISOLITIC—Possessing a structure like an agglutination of peas.

PITCH—See *Plunge*.

PLUNGE—In folding, the dip (where this is appreciable) along the crest of an anticline or the trough of a syncline. Until about twenty years ago, 'pitch' was used for this quantity and is perhaps still to be preferred, but it is now often restricted to another quantity of minor interest.

PLUTONIC ROCKS—Coarsely crystalline igneous rocks formed by the slow cooling of a large, deep-seated molten mass. The commonest rock-type is granite.

PORPHYRITIC—A texture of igneous rocks in which there is a sharp distinction between larger crystals and a finer-grained or glassy groundmass. Most marked in certain rhyolites and hypabyssal rocks.

POTHOLE—A bowl-shaped or cylindrical hollow scooped out or bored in the rocky beds of a stream or on the seashore by pebbles swirled round by eddies or breaking waves. (Also used for a 'swallow-hole' in a limestone surface.)

PRIMARY STRUCTURES—Structures resulting from the original formation of the rocks; eg, bedding, unconformity.

PYRITE, PYRITES, IRON PYRITES—The brass-yellow mineral, iron sulphide FeS_2. Copper pyrites is the double sulphide of copper and iron ($CuFeS_2$).

PYROCLASTIC ROCKS—Accumulations of solid rock-materials ejected, as either liquid or solid particles, in a volcanic eruption. The term is usually applied to such an accumulation of a past geological age, now compact and hard.

QUARTZ—The mineral silica (SiO_2). Occurs in the acid igneous rocks and as the sand grains in sandstones.

QUARTZITE—A hard sedimentary or metamorphic rock composed of quartz.

RADIOMETRIC—The kind of measurement determining the absolute (as distinct from the relative) age of certain minerals, and thus of certain rocks, on the basis of the known rate of radioactive change.

RHYOLITE—Acid lava

RHYTHMIC SEQUENCE—A small-scale sequence of beds repeated over and over again. (A larger scale repetition is usually called a 'cyclic sequence'.)

RIBBON BANDING—See *Band.*

RINGERS—Hard beds that 'ring' when struck. Applied particularly to the flags of the Lingula Flags series.

ROCK—An aggregate of mineral particles. (But coal, formed of carbonised organic material, is also certainly a rock.)

SANDSTONE—A hard rock resulting from the consolidation of a deposit of sand.

SCARP—Though in a general way this is any abrupt slope in the landscape, it more particularly refers to that formed by a resistant stratum where the rising dip-slope becomes sharply truncated by erosion.

SCHIST—A finely crystalline metamorphic rock, with 'foliation' resulting from the parallel disposition of lamellar minerals, particularly mica. Foliation structure resembles a mass of compressed (and of course hardened) leaves. Hence 'schistosity' and the adjective 'schistose'.

SECONDARY STRUCTURES—Deformation structures resulting from 'tectonic' forces: folding, faulting, slaty cleavage, etc.

SECTION—In ordinary geology, as distinct from petrography ('thin section'), there the several senses: (1) an individual exposure, in which the rocks are seen 'cut through'; (2) a series of exposures of a rock-succession, such as one along a strip of coast; (3) the reconstruction, from the information on a geological map or from a special traverse across the country, of the vertical section of the structure along a particular line.

SEDIMENTARY ROCKS—Strictly, these are hard rocks formed by the consolidation of a sediment. But usually all rocks are included other than the purely igneous and the completely metamorphic; such as

N

shelly accumulations in the sea and rocks of wind-borne origin on land.

SHALE—A mudstone splitting or flaking along planes of lamination; this lamination being fine-scale bedding.

SHATTER-BELT—A belt of shattered faulted rock.

SILICIFICATION—Mineral replacement by silica.

SILL—An igneous intrusive sheet among stratified rocks, following the stratification. Typically intruded more or less horizontally.

SILTSTONE—A convenient term for a type of lithology intermediate between a mudstone and a sandstone.

SINISTRAL FAULT—See *Tear fault*.

SLATE—In strict geological usage, a fine-grained rock which splits readily along planes of 'slaty cleavage' which has been imposed on the rock as a result of lateral pressure. This cleavage is at right angles to the pressure and is to be clearly distinguished from the lamination of shales.

SLICKENSIDE—A fault surface scratched and polished by the fault movement; the surface is often mineralised.

SLIP-SCRATCH—A scratch on a bedding surface produced by the slipping of a contiguous bedding surface, in adjustment during folding or from some other cause. Such scratches may be hooked, curved, or angular, and occur as a set.

SOLE-MARK—A mark on the (original) undersurfaces of a bed.

SOLID GEOLOGY—The geological features of the rocks underlying superficial deposits.

SPECIES—In the naming of fossils, as of living animals and plants, the species comprises all those, usually innumerable, individuals that are so much alike as to warrant their being called by the same name. Specific characters tend to keep distinct by interbreeding within the species but not between one species and another.

SPILITE—A basic lava rich in the element sodium, usually spotted with gas-bubbles filled with secondary minerals. Occurs chiefly in the form of pillow-lava.

STRATIFIED—Disposed in layers. It usually implies that the layers are layers of sedimentation, and the term 'stratified rock' definitely implies a sedimentary rock. Hence 'stratification'.

STRATIGRAPHY—The descriptive facts about strata: their occurrence, lithology, fossil content, succession, and mutual relations, and their classification with a view to arranging them in chronological order. Hence 'stratigraphical'.

STRATUM—See *Bed*.

STRIKE—The direction on a structural surface, particularly a bedding-surface, at right angles to the dip. A line in that direction will be horizontal.

STRIKE-FAULT—A fault aligned in the direction of the strike of the beds it affects.

STRIKE-SLIP—In faulting, the component of movement along the strike of the fault.

SUBAERIAL—On land, under the atmosphere; in distinction from 'marine'. Particularly as 'subaerial erosion'.

SUB-VOLCANIC ROCKS—Small bodies of igneous intrusive rock formed not far below the earth's surface and directly connected with volcanic rocks formed on the surface; eg a rock formed from magma 'feeding' a volcanic vent. Petrographically the rock-types are the same as those of volcanic rocks.

SUPERIMPOSED DRAINAGE—A river drainage pattern that was initiated and developed as a result of the uplift of a rock series now eroded away, exposing an underlying structure to which the drainage pattern is unrelated.

SUPERPOSITION—The 'order of superposition' is the order of rocks in upward succession as they were originally deposited.

SYNCLINE—A downfold of a series of rocks.

SYNCLINORIUM—A compound syncline.

SYSTEM—In stratigraphy, a major general division of the whole succession.

TEAR FAULT—A fault resulting from movement that was chiefly or entirely horizontal, along the fault-surface (strike-slip), not up-and-down (dip-slip). Also called 'transcurrent fault', 'wrench fault'. A 'sinistral fault' of this kind is one where the relative movement was to the left on the far side when viewed from either side, the other case being a 'dextral fault'.

TECTONIC—Structural; usually referring to the processes and results of movements and pressures within the earth's crust.

THRUST FAULT—A fault, usually not steeply inclined, in which one side has been thrust over the other. Also called an 'overthrust' or simply 'thrust'. Hence 'thrust-plane'.

TRANSCURRENT FAULT—See *Tear fault*.

TRANSGRESSIVE SILL—A sill that does not keep strictly to one stratigraphical horizon.

TRANSPRESSION FAULT—A compressive fault combining both transcurent (tear) movement and overthrusting.

TRILOBITES (Trilobita)—A group of extinct arthropods, confined to the Palaeozoic and very characteristic of the Lower Palaeozoic.

TUFF—See *Volcanic ash*.

UNCONFORMABLE, UNCONFORMITY—When an upper formation or series or rocks is laid down on the eroded, truncated edges of a lower series, the upper series is 'unconformable' to the lower. The structures of the two series are separate. This discordant relationship is 'unconformity' and the surface of discordance is 'an unconformity'. In the usual case, the outcrops of the base of the upper series (that is, the outcrop of the unconformity) cuts across, 'oversteps', the outcrops of the members of the lower series. When upper members of the upper series spread farther than the lower members, we have 'overlap' within that series. Unconformity also results when sedimentary rocks are laid down on an eroded surface of igneous rock. Superficial deposits are unconformable to the underlying 'solid' rocks, though the term is seldom used in that case as such a relationship goes without saying.

UNIFORMITARIANISM—The fundamental principle that the geological processes of past, present, and future are of a similar nature.

VEIN—In geology, usually a 'mineral vein'; one mineral or several together occurring along a line or over a surface within a rock-mass.

VOLCANIC ASH—The finer pyroclastic material shot out of a volcano. It results from explosion, not burning. The term is sometimes used for this (hardened) material of a past geological age, but 'tuff' is then more precise.

VOLCANIC ROCKS—Rocks resulting from volcanic action; either lava-flows or fragmental (pyroclastic) accumulations.

WASH-OUT—An interruption in the continuity of a bed, or part of a bed, due to contemporaneous erosion.

WRENCH FAULT—See *Tear fault.*

ZINC BLENDE—The dark brown mineral with a resinous lustre, zinc sulphide (ZnS).

ZONE—In stratigraphy, a small division characterised by a certain assemblage of fossils of which one is selected as index species.

Bibliography

Abbreviations of periodicals and series

AS   Advancement of Science
BA   British Association [Report]
BBMG   Bulletin of the British Museum (Natural History):
        Geology
BV   Bulletin Volcanologique [Naples]
G   Geography
GAG   Geologists' Association Guides
GJ   Geological Journal [Continuation of LMGJ]
GM   Geological Magazine
GR   Geographical Review [American Geographical Society]
IGC   International Geological Congress [Report]
IBG   Institute of British Geographers [Transactions and
        papers]
JE   Journal of Ecology
JGS   Journal of the Geological Society of London
        [Continuation of QJGS]
LMGJ   Liverpool and Manchester Geological Journal
MGS   Memoirs of the Geological Survey of Great Britain
N   Nature
NW   Nature in Wales
PGA   Proceedings of the Geologists' Association
PGS   Proceedings of the Geological Society of London
PLGS   Proceedings of the Liverpool Geological Society
PTRS   Philosophical Transactions of the Royal Society of
        London
PYGS   Proceedings of the Yorkshire Geological Society
QJGS   Quarterly Journal of the Geological Society of London
SPRDS   Scientific Proceedings of the Royal Dublin Society
TRSE   Transactions of the Royal Society of Edinburgh
WGQ   Welsh Geological Quarterly

Allen, J. R. L. 'The sedimentation and palaeogeography of the Old Red Sandstone of Anglesey', *PYGS*, 35 (1965), 139-85

Andrew, A. R. 'The geology of the Dolgelley gold-belt', *GM*, 47 (1910), 159-71, 201-11

Bailey, E. 'The Mona Complex in Lleyn and its relation to the Ordovician', *AS*, 11 (1954), 108

Bassett, D. A. *Bibliography and index of geology and allied sciences for Wales and the Welsh Borders, 1897-1958*, Cardiff (1961)

Bibliography and index of geology and allied sciences for Wales and the Welsh Borders, 1536-1896, Cardiff (1963)

'Lists of papers, books, theses, etc on the geology of Wales and the Welsh Borders, 1959-60, 1961-2, 1963-4, *LMGJ*, 3 (1962-6), 33-40; *GJ*, 4, 35-42; 5, 7-14

'The Welsh Palaeozoic Geosyncline: a review of recent work on stratigraphy and sedimentation'. In Johnson and Stewart (1963), 35-69

A source-book of geological, geomorphological, and soil maps for Wales and the Welsh Borders (1800-1966), Cardiff (1967)

'A bibliography and index of geological excursion guides and reports for Wales and the Welsh Borders, *WGQ*, 3 (no 1) (1967), 3-23

'Some of the major structures of early Palaeozoic age in Wales and the Welsh Borderland'. In A. Wood (1969), 67-116

and Walton, E. K. 'The Hell's Mouth Grits: Cambrian greywackes in St Tudwal's Peninsula', *QJGS*, 116 (1960), 85-110

Whittington, H. B., and Williams, A. 'The stratigraphy of the Bala district', *QJGS*, 122 (1966), 219-71

Bates, D. E. B. 'The geology of Parys Mountain', *WGQ*, 2 (no 1) (1966), 27-9

'The Lower Palaeozoic brachiopod and trilobite faunas of Anglesey, *BBMG*, 16 (no 4) (1968)

'Some aspects of the Arenig faunas of Wales'. In A. Wood (1969), 155-9

'A field guide to the Mynydd Bodafon—Lligwy Bay area', *WGQ*, 5 (no 1) (1969), 17-23

'The stratigraphy of the Ordovician rocks of Anglesey', *GJ*, 8 (1972), 29-58

Bathurst, R. G. C. and others. 'Geology around the university towns: Liverpool', *GAG* 6 (1965)

Beavon, R. V. 'The succession and structure east of the Glaslyn River', *QJGS*, 119 (1963), 479-512

Belt, T. 'On the "Lingula Flags" or "Festiniog Group" of the Dolgelley district,' *GM*, 4 (1867-8), 493-5,536-43; 5: 5-11

Boswell, P. G. H. *The Middle Silurian rocks of North Wales* (1949)

Bowen, E. G. and others. *Geography at Aberystwyth*, Cardiff (1969)

Brenchley, P. 'The relationship between Caradocian volcanicity and sedimentation in North Wales'. In A. Wood (1969), 181-202

Bromley, A. V. 'Intrusive quartz latites in the Blaenau-Ffestiniog area', *GJ*, 4, (1965), 247-56
'Acid plutonic igneous activity in the Ordovician of North Wales'. In A. Wood (1969), 387-408

Cattermole, P. 'A preliminary geochemical study of the Mynydd Penarfynydd intrusion, Rhiw igneous complex, south-west Lleyn'. In A. Wood (1969), 435-46

Challinor, J. 'Fossils in Wales', *NW*, 1 (1955), 167-9
'Geological research in Cardiganshire, 1842-1967', *WGQ*, 4 (1962) (nos 2 & 3), 3-37
'The Pre-Cambrian in Cambria', *IGC*, session 24 (1972), in the press

Clark, J. and Hughes, T. McK. *The Life and letters of the Reverend Adam Sedgwick*, Cambridge (1890)

Condry, W. M. *The Snowdonia National Park* (1966)
Exploring Wales (1970)

Cowie, J. W., Rushton, A. W. A., and Stubblefield, C. J. *Cambrian: Geological Society report* (1972)

Cox, A. H. 'The geology of the Cader Idris range', *QJGS*, 81 (1925), 539-94
and Lewis, H. P. 'Field meeting in the Dolgelley district', *PGA*, 56 (1945), 59-81
and Wells, A. K. 'The Lower Palaeozoic rocks of the Arthog-Dolgelley district', *QJGS*, 76 (1920), 254-324
'The geology of the Dolgelley district and the visit to Dolgelley', *PGA*, 38 (1927), 265-331

Crimes, T. P. 'A facies analysis of the Arenig of Western Lleyn', PGA, 81 (1970), 271-39

Davies, D. A. B. 'The Ordovician rocks of the Trefriw district', *QJGS*, 92 (1936), 62-90

Davies, R. G. 'The Pen-y-gader dolerite and its metasomatic effects on the Llyn-y-gader sediments', GM, 93 (1956), 153-72
'The Cader Idris Granophyre and its associated rocks', QJGS, 115 (1959), 189-216
'A geology of the Cader Idris area: field itinerary with theoretical explanations', WGQ, 3 (no 2) (1967), 10-22

Davis, J. E. 'On the geology of the neighbourhood of Tremadoc', QJGS, 2 (1846), 70-75

Davis, W. M. 'Glacial erosion in North Wales', QJGS, 65 (1909), 281-350

Elles, G. L. 'Some graptolite zones in the Arenig rocks of Wales', GM, 41 (1904), 199-211
'The relation of the Ordovician and Silurian rocks of Conway', QJGS, 65 (1909), 169-94
'The Bala country: its structure and rocks succession', QJGS, 78 (1922), 132-75

Embleton, C. 'North-eastern Wales [Glaciation]'. In C. A. Lewis (1970), 59-82   ,

Evans, E. P. 'Cader Idris: a study of certain plant communities in south-west Merionethshire', JE, 20 (1932), 1-52

Fearnsides, W. G. 'On the geology of Arenig Fawr and Moel Llyfnant, QJGS, 61 (1905), 608-40
'Excursion to North Wales', PGA, 21 (1910), 368-90
'The Tremadoc Slates and associated rocks of south-east Caernarvonshire', QJGS, 66 (1910), 142-88
'Excursion to Portmadoc and Criccieth district', PGA, 23 (1912), 199-217
and Davies, W. 'The geology of Deudraeth', QJGS, 99 (1943), 247-76

Fitch, F. J. 'Ignimbrite volcanism in North Wales', BV, 30 (1967), 199-220
'Field meeting in Snowdonia', JGS, 127 (1971), 533-4

Fitches, W. R. 'Polyphase deformation structures in the Welsh Caledonides near Aberystwyth', GM, 109 (1972), 149-55

George, T. N. British Regional geology: North Wales, 3rd edn (1961) (previous editions by B. Smith and T. N. George, 1935, 1948)
British regional geology: South Wales, 3rd edn (1970); (previous edns by J. Pringle and T. N. George, 1937, 1948)

Greenly, E. The geology of Anglesey, MGS (1919)

Geological itineraries in Anglesey. Liverpool, privately printed (1921)

'The Lower Carboniferous rocks of the Menain region of Caernarvonshire', *QJGS*, 84 (1928), 382-439

'The age of the mountains of Snowdonia', *QJGS*, 94 (1938), 117-24

'The Red Measures of the Menaian region of Caernarvonshire', *QJGS*, 94 (1938), 331-45

'Notes on the glacial phenomena of Arvon', *QJGS*, 97 (1941), 163-78

'The Ordovician rocks of Arvon', *QJGS*, 100 (1944), 75-83

'The Arvonian rocks of Arvon', *QJGS*, 100 (1944), 269-87

Harker, A. *The Bala Volcanic series of Caernarvonshire*, Cambridge (1889)

Harper, J. C. 'The Ordovician succession near Llanystumdwy', *LMGJ*, 1 (1956), 385-93

Howell, B. F. and Stubblefield, C. J. 'A revision of the fauna of the North Welsh *Conocoryphe viola* beds implying a Lower Cambrian age', *GM*, 87 (1950), 1-16

Hughes, E. W. 'On the geology of the district from Cil-y-coed to the St Annes-Llanllyfni ridge', *GM*, 54 (1917), 12-25

James, D. M. D. 'The Nant-y-moch formation, Plynlimon inlier', *JGS*, 127 (1971), 177-86

Jehu, R. M. 'The geology of the district around Towyn and Abergynolwyn', *QJGS*, 82 (1926), 465-89

Jehu, T. J. 'The glacial deposits of western Caernarvonshire', *TRSE*, 47 (1909), 17-56

Jennings, A. V. and Williams, G. J. 'Manod and the Moelwyns', *QJGS*, 47 (1891), 368-83

Johnson, M. R. W. and Stewart, F. H. *The British Caledonides*, Edinburgh (1963)

Jones, B. 'The geology of the Fairbourne-Llwyngwril district', *QJGS*, 89 (1933), 145-71

Jones, O. T. 'The Hartfell-Valentian succession in the district around Plynlimon and Pont Erwyd', *QJGS*, 65 (1909), 463-537

'The geological structure of Central Wales and the adjoining regions', *QJGS*, 68 (1912), 328-44

'The mining district of north Cardiganshire and west Montgomeryshire', *MGS* (1922)

'On the sliding and slumping of submarine sediments in Den-

P

bighshire during the Ludlow period', *QJGS*, 93 (1937), 241-83

'On the evolution of a geosyncline', *QJGS*, 94 (1938), lx-cx

'The geology of the Colwyn Bay district; a study of submarine slumping during the Salopian period', *QJGS*, 95 (1939), 335-82

'The trends of geological structures in relation to directions of maximum compression' (includes a section on the Merioneth Dome), *AS*, 11 (1954), 102-6

'The geological evolution of Wales', *QJGS*, 111 (1956), 323-51 and Pugh, W. J. 'The geology of the district around Machynlleth and the Llyfnant valley', *QJGS*, 71 (1915), 343-85

'The geology of the districts around Machynlleth and Aberystwyth, with an account of a field meeting', *PGA*, 46 (1935), 247-300, 413-28

Keeping, W. 'The geology of Central Wales', *QJGS*, 37 (1881), 141-77

Lake, P. and Reynolds, S. H. 'The geology of Mynydd-y-Gader, Dolgelley', *QJGS*, 68 (1912), 345-62

Lewis, C. A. (ed). *The glaciations of Wales and adjoining regions* (1970)

Lewis, H. P. 'On *Bolopora undosa*: a rock-building bryozoan with phosphatised skeleton, from the basal Arenig rocks of Ffestiniog', *QJGS*, 82 (1926), 412-27

'Ordovician succession at the south-west end of the Aran range', *BA* (1936), 351-2

Lewis, W. J. *Lead mining in Wales*, Cardiff (1967)

An Illustrated history of Cardiganshire, Cumdeithas Lyfrau Ceredigion (1970)

Lovell, J. P. B. 'The palaeogeographical significance of lateral variations in the ratio of sandstone to shale and other features of the Aberystwyth Grits', *GM*, 107 (1970), 147-58

Matley, C. A. 'The geology of Bardsey Island', *QJGS*, 69 (1913), 514-33

'The Pre-Cambrian complex and associated rocks of south-western Lleyn', *QJGS*, 84 (1928), 440-504

'The geology of the country around Mynydd Rhiw, and Sarn, south-western Lleyn', *QJGS*, 88 (1932), 238-73

'A 50ft coastal terrace and other late-glacial phenomena in the Lleyn peninsula', *PGA*, 47 (1936), 221-33

'The geology of the country around Pwllheli, Llanbedrog and Madryn', *QJGS*, 94 (1938), 555-606

and Heard, A. 'The geology of the country around Bodfean', *QJGS*, 86 (1930), 130-68

Nicholas, T. C. and Heard, A. 'Field meeting to the western part of the Lleyn Peninsula', *PGA*, 50 (1939), 83-100

and Smith, B. 'The age of the Sarn granite', *QJGS*, 92 (1936), 188-200

and Wilson, T. S. 'The Harlech Dome, north of the Barmouth estuary', *QJGS*, 102 (1946), 1-40

Miller, A. A. 'Some physical features related to the river development in the Dolgelley district', *PGA* 57 (1946), 174-203

Monckton, H. W. and Herries, R. S. (eds). *Geology in the Field* (Jubilee volume of the Geologists' Association) (1910)

Morris, T. O. and Fearnsides, W. G. 'The stratigraphy and structure of the Cambrian slate-belt of Nantlle', *QJGS*, 82 (1926), 250-303

Morton, G. H. 'The Carboniferous Limestone of the country around Llandudno', *QGJS*, 54 (1898), 382-400

Neaverson, E. 'The Carboniferous rocks between Llandudno and Colwyn Bay', *PLGS*, 17 (1937) 115-35 [And other papers on the Carboniferous Limestone of North Wales, 1930-46, *PLGS*, 15-19]

Nicholas, T. C. 'The geology of the St Tudwal's Peninsula', *QJGS*, 71 (1915), 83-143

'Notes on the trilobite fauna of the Middle Cambrian of the St Tudwal's Peninsula', *QJGS*, 71 (1915), 451-72

North, F. J. *Coal, and the coalfields in Wales*. 2nd edn (1931) (1st edition, 1926), Cardiff

The slates of Wales. 3rd edn (1946) (previous editions, 1925, 1927), Cardiff

'Geology and the physical background of Snowdonia'. In North, Campbell, and Scott (1949), 1-156

Mining for metals in Wales (1962), Cardiff

Campbell, B., and Scott, R. *Snowdonia: the National Park of Wales* (1949)

Phillips, W. J. 'The movement and consolidation of magmas: illustrated with reference to the succession of Ordovician strata and igneous rocks in the Arthog-Dolgellau district', *WGQ*, 2 (no 2) (1966), 3-9

Pugh, W. J. 'The geology of the district around Corris and Aberllefenni', *QJGS*, 79 (1923), 508-45

'The geology of the district around Dinas Mawddwy', *QJGS*, 84 (1928), 345-81

'The geology of the district betwen Llanymawddwy and Llan-uwchllyn', *QJGS*, 85 (1929), 241-306

Pulfrey, W. 'The iron-ore oolites and pisolites of North Wales', *QJGS*, 89 (1933), 401-30

Ramsay, A. C. *The old glaciers of Switzerland and North Wales* (1860)

The geology of North Wales. 2nd edn (1881) (1st edn, 1866), MGS

Rast, N. 'Ordovician volcanoes of North and Central Wales: volcanic rocks and their distribution', *NW*, 6 (1960), 111-16

'Mid-Ordovician structures in south-western Snowdonia', *LMGJ*, 2 (1961), 645-52

'Textural evidence for the origin of ignimbrites', *LMGJ*, 3 (1962), 97-108

'The relationship between Ordovician structure and volcanicity in Wales'. In Wood (1969), 305-35

Beavon, R. V., and Fitch, F. J. 'Sub-aerial volcanicity in Snowdonia', *N*, 181 (1958), 508

('Rast, Fitch, and Beavon'). 'The nomenclature and diognostic characters of ignimbrites, with reference to Snowdonia', (abstract, with discussion), *PGS* (no 1571) (1959), 116-21

('Beavon, Fitch, and Rast'). 'Nomenclature and diagnostic characters of ignimbrites with reference to Snowdonia', *LMGJ*, 2 (1961), 600-11

Roberts, B. 'Succession and structure in the Llwyd Mawr Syncline', *GJ*, 5 (1967), 369-90

'The Llwyd Mawr Ignimbrite and its associated volcanic rocks'. In Wood (1969), 337-56

Salter, J. W. *A catalogue of the collection of Cambrian and Silurian fossils contained in the Geological Museum of the University of Cambridge.* Cambridge (1873)

Sedgwick, A. 'A synopsis of the English series of stratified rocks inferior to the Old Red Sandstone', *PGS*, 2 (1838), 675-85

'Outline of geological structure of North Wales', *PGS*, 4 (1843), 212-24

'On the comparative classification of the fossiliferous strata of North Wales, with the corresponding deposits of Cumberland, Westmoreland, and Lancashire', *QJGS*, 1 (1845), 442-50

'On the classification of the fossiliferous slates of North Wales etc', *QJGS*, 3 (1847), 133-64

'On the classification and nomenclature of the Lower Palaeozoic rocks of England and Wales', *QJGS*, 8 (1852), 136-68

Preface to Salter (1873), ix-xxxiii

and M'Coy. *British Palaeozoic rocks and fossils*, Cambridge (1855)

Shackleton, R. M. 'The structural evolution of North Wales', *LMGJ*, 1 (1953), 261-97

'The structure and succession of Anglesey and the Lleyn Peninsula', *AS*, 11 (1954), 106-8

'Notes on the structure and relations of the Pre-Cambrian and Ordovician rocks of south-western Lleyn', *LMGJ*, 1 (1958), 400-9

'The stratigraphy of the Moel Hebog district between Snowdon and Tremadoc', *LMGJ*, 2 (1959), 216-52

'The Pre-Cambrian of North Wales'. In A. Wood (1969) 1-22

Sharpe, D. 'Contributions to the geology of North Wales', *QJGS*, 2 (1846), 283-316

Skevington, D. 'The classification of the Ordovician system in Wales'. In A. Wood (1969), 161-179

Smyth, L. B. 'A contribution to the geology of Great Ormes Head', *SPRDS*, 18 (1926), 141-64

Stubblefield, C. J. 'Cambrian palaeogeography in Britain', *IGC*, session 20, 1 (1956), 1-43

Thomas, T. M. 'Wales: land of mines and quarries', *GR*, 46 (1955), 59-81

The mineral wealth of Wales and its exploitation, Edinburgh and London (1961)

'The imprint of structural grain on the micro-relief of the Welsh uplands', *GJ*, 7 (1970), 69-100

Tremlett, W. E. (Papers on the geology of eastern Lleyn), *LMGJ*, 3 (1962-5), 157-76; *GJ*, 4, 207-23, 435-48

'Caradocian volcanicity in the Lleyn peninsula'. In Wood (1969), 357-85

Watson, E. 'Glacial land-forms in the Cader Idris area', *G*, 45 (1960), 27-38

'The glacial morphology of the Tal-y-llyn valley', *IBG* (1962), 15-31

'The periglacial landscape of the Aberystwyth region'. In Bowen and others (1969), 35-49

'The Cardigan Bay area [Glaciation]'. In C. A. Lewis (1970), 125-45

Wedd, C. B. and others. *The geology of the country around Wrexham*, MGS (1927-8), parts I and II

Wells, A. K. 'The geology of the Rhobell Fawr district', *GJGS*, 81 (1925), 463-538

Whittard, W. F. 'The stratigraphy of the Valentian rocks of Shropshire: the Longmynd-Shelve and Breidden outcrops', *QJGS*, 88 (1932), 859-902

Whittow, J. B. and Ball, D. F. 'North-west Wales [Glaciation]'. In C. A. Lewis (1970), 21-58

Williams, A. 'Ordovician faunal provinces with references to brachiopod distribution'. In A. Wood (1969), 117-54

Williams, D. 'The geology of the country between Nant Peris and Nant Ffrancon', *QJGS*, 86 (1930), 191-233

and Ramsay, J. G. 'Geology of some classic British areas: Snowdonia', 2nd edn (1st edn, 1959), *GAG*, 28 (1968)

Williams, H. 'The igneous rocks of the Capel Curig district', *PLGS*, 13 (1922), 166-206

'The geology of Snowdon', *QJGS*, 83 (1927), 346-431

'Field meeting in the Snowdon district', *PGA*, 41 (1930), 190-205

and Bulman. 'The geology of the Dolwyddelan Syncline', *QJGS*, 87 (1931), 425-58

Wills, L. J. 'The geology of the Llangollen district and excursion to Llangollen', *PGA*, 31 (1920), 1-25

Wood, A. (ed). *The Pre-Cambrian and Lower Palaeozoic rocks of Wales*, Cardiff (1969)

and Smith, A. J. 'The sedimentation and sedimentary history of the Aberystwyth Grits, *QJGS*, 114 (1958), 163-95

Wood, D. 'The base and correlation of the Cambrian rocks of North Wales'. In A. Wood (1969), 47-66

Woodland, A. W. 'Petrological studies in the Harlech Grit series', *GM*, 75 (1938), 366-82, 440-54, 529-39

'The petrography and petrology of the Lower Cambrian manganese ore of west Merionethshire', *QJGS*, 95 (1939), 1-35

'The petrography and petrology of the manganese ore of the Rhiw district', *PGA*, 50 (1939), 205-22 (ed.) *The Llanbedr (Mochras Farm) borehole* (Institute of Geological Sciences report), HMSO (1971)

MAPS OF THE GEOLOGICAL SURVEY
(INSTITUTE OF GEOLOGICAL SCIENCES)

10-mile (scale, 1in=9.7 miles). Great Britain, in two sheets. Sheet 2 (south sheet), first published in 1948. Although our area occupies only a very small part, this map shows all essential details, and is the most up-to-date for our area. The map accompanying the 3rd (1961) edition of the Regional Geology handbook for North Wales (scale, 8 miles to 1in) is based on it.

¼in (scale, 1in=4 miles). Sheet 9 with 10. A reprint of the 2nd (1930) edition was issued in 1968, but certain revisions of knowledge made between these years are not incorporated. It is the largest-scale map available for our whole area.

1in (scale, 1in=1 mile). The greater part of North Wales is shown on the 'old series' sheets published between 1848 and 1852. Parts of Denbighshire and Flintshire are on two 'old series' sheets published in 1885 and 1886. The only 'new series' sheets are the one sheet of the whole of Anglesey, numbered 92 and 93 (1920), and three sheets covering the North Wales Coalfield and adjacent parts, 102, 121, 137 (1924, 1927, 1928, with some later reprints). The quarter-inch map is a reduction from these original surveys, with very little modification even from those published in the middle of the last century.

Tectonic map of Great Britain and Northern Ireland (scale, 1in =25 miles). This map, although our area on it is on such a small scale, shows the fold axes, faults, and unconformities, proved and conjectured. First published in 1966.

Appendix: Ordovician and Silurian Fossil Zones

GRAPTOLITE ZONES OF THE ORDOVICIAN SYSTEM

Upper Bala (Ashgill series) { Dicellograptus anceps
Dicellograptus complanatus

Lower Bala (Caradoc series) { Pleurograptus linearus
Dicranograptus clingani
Climacograptus wilsoni
Climacograptus peltifer
Nemagraptus gracilis

Llandeilo series Glytograptus teretiusculus

Llanvirn series { Didymograptus murchisoni
Didymograptus bifidus

Arenig series { Didymograptus hirundo
Didymograptus extensus

GRAPTOLITE ZONES OF THE SILURIAN SYSTEM

Ludlow series
- Monograptus leintwardinensis
- Monograptus tumescens
- Monograptus scanicus
- Monograptus nilssoni
- Monograptus vulgaris

Wenlock series
- Cyrtograptus lundgreni
- Cyrtograptus rigidus
- Cyrograptus linnarssoni
- Cyrtograptus symmetricus
- Monograptus riccartonensis
- Cyrtograptus murchisoni

Llandovery series
- Monograptus crenulatus
- Monograptus griestonensis
- Monograptus crispus
- Monograptus turriculatus
- Monograptus sedgwicki
- Cephalograptus cometa
- Monograptus convolutus
- Monograptus lepotheca
- Diplograptus magnus   } Monograptus communis
- Monograptus triangulatus
- Monograptus cyphus
- Monograptus acinaces
- Monograptus atavus
- Akidograptus acuminatus
- Glyptograptus persculptus

Index